APOLLO: LUNAR LANDING

APOLLO: LUNAR LANDING

James J. Haggerty

RAND McNALLY & COMPANY

Chicago • New York • San Francisco

The Author wishes to thank the following for the excellent photographs made available for this book:

  The Apollo astronauts
  National Aeronautics and Space Administration
  North American Rockwell Corporation, Space Division and
    Rocketdyne Division
  U.S. Naval Observatory
  Grumman Aircraft Engineering Corporation
  Avco Corporation, Space Systems Division
  The Boeing Company

A WALLACE B. BLACK PRODUCTION

Table of Contents

Chapter 1   Apollo to the Moon   8

Chapter 2   The Saturn V Launch Vehicle   16

Chapter 3   The Basic Spacecraft   36

Chapter 4   The Lunar Module   52

Chapter 5   The Earth-based Complex   64

Chapter 6   Samples of the Moon   84

Chapter 7   Apollo's Pathfinders   90

Chapter 8   Rehearsals for the Moon   96

Chapter 9   Eagle on the Moon   120

Apollo Glossary   153

Commemorative plaque attached to a landing leg on *Eagle*, the Lunar Module.

"THAT'S ONE SMALL STEP FOR A MAN,
ONE GIANT LEAP FOR MANKIND."

Astronaut Neil Armstrong, at the
moment of stepping onto
the moon's surface, July 20, 1969

"Because of what you have done, the heavens have become a part of man's world. As you talk to us from the Sea of Tranquillity, it inspires us to redouble our efforts to bring peace and tranquillity to earth. For one priceless moment in the whole history of man, all of the people on this earth are truly one—one in their pride in what you have done and one in our prayers that you will return safely to Earth."

President Richard M. Nixon to the
Apollo 11 astronauts on the moon

Apollo to the Moon

CHAPTER 1

BELIEVE THAT THIS NATION should commit itself to achieving the goal, before the decade is out, of landing a man on the moon and returning him safely to earth. No single space project in this period will be more impressive to mankind, or more important to the long-range exploration of space; and none so difficult or expensive to accomplish."

With these words, addressed to a joint session of Congress on May 25, 1961, President John F. Kennedy formally launched Project Apollo, the greatest technological undertaking in history. For as long as he had had the intelligence to contemplate it, man had dreamed of visiting earth's ancient satellite; now, in the second half of the twentieth century, a leader of the American people had accepted the challenge.

It was a bold commitment, even a presumptuous one. Flight to the moon represented a giant step several orders of magnitude beyond the most ambitious space venture then on the agenda. The Space Age was in only its fourth year. The Soviet Union had sent a man into orbit but the United States had not; its total experience in manned extraterrestrial operations consisted of a single 15-minute flight. Even in the less exacting area of unmanned space research the United States' record was something less than spectacular. There was little in the American background to promise success for so far-reaching an enterprise.

However, the commitment—and the accomplishment—was necessary for the maintenance of a strong American diplomatic posture. The United States' image as technological leader of the world had been tarnished by the nation's failure to match the consistent Soviet space success. The loss of international prestige was more than just an embarrassment; it had serious political overtones in the cold war between conflicting ideologies.

"The earth from here is a
grand oasis in the big
vastness of space"—Astronaut
Lovell on the first manned
voyage around the moon.

Among the peoples of the world, there was dwindling confidence in America's ability to contain the threat of Soviet aggression, and in the bloodless struggle the support of free men was as important to the United States as its arsenal of deterrent weapons. If the nation was to recoup its prestigial fortunes, there was urgent need for a sweeping, dramatic demonstration that it was still technologically superior to any power.

Project Apollo provided that demonstration. Under the aegis of the National Aeronautics and Space Administration (NASA), the government assembled a task force that numbered at its peak more than 350,000 people. The development of the sophisticated hardware needed to send men across the hostile ocean of space proceeded at a rate that even those intimately connected with the program found hard to believe.

Within a year of the Kennedy pronouncement, some of the Apollo equipment was already being ground-tested. By late 1963 preliminary flight tests were under way and in 1965 the first complete spacecraft was delivered to NASA for unmanned test. In October, 1968, a human crew first went aloft in Apollo and only two months thereafter came the magnificent flight of Apollo 8 into orbit around the moon.

This incredibly rapid progression from concept to accomplishment was all the more remarkable for the scope of the program. Apollo is a great deal more than simply an extension of its predecessors, Mercury and Gemini. From the standpoint of design experience, it profited little from these earlier projects; in fact, Apollo's basic configuration was drawn up before the first Mercury orbital flight and before Gemini was even initiated. Mercury and Gemini, restricted to operations within a few hundred miles of earth's surface, pioneered the basic techniques of manned space flight. But Apollo demanded an entirely new order of technological advance because it was designed to perform in an alien gravity a quarter of a million miles distant. This single requirement compounded every element of the developmental task and forced American ingenuity to unprecedented levels of accomplishment.

As President Kennedy predicted, Apollo has been expensive. The complete program, which envisions 10 or more manned lunar landings at as many different sites, will run well above $25 billion before the last bill is paid. Yet future historians will no doubt find that the gain was greater than the expenditure.

Already the program has paid a major dividend in prestige re-won, an asset of incalculable value at the international bargaining table. But the potential benefits, to mankind in general and Americans in particular, are far broader in scope.

U.S. MANNED SPACE FLIGHT PROGRAM

MERCURY

ONE-MAN CREW

SPACECRAFT: 6'10" high, plus Adapter and
Launch Escape Tower
4265 pounds
Spacesuit environment

LAUNCH VEHICLE: Atlas, 388,000 pounds thrust

MISSION: answering basic questions about man in space; earth orbital

FIRST MANNED FLIGHT: Feb. 20, 1962

GEMINI

TWO-MAN CREW

SPACECRAFT: 11'4" high, plus Adapter
Module
8360 pounds
Shirtsleeve environment

LAUNCH VEHICLE: Titan II, 430,000 pounds thrust

MISSION: maneuvering man and craft in space; earth orbital

FIRST MANNED FLIGHT: March 23, 1965

APOLLO

THREE-MAN CREW

SPACECRAFT: 10' 7" high, plus Service
Module, Lunar Module,
Launch Escape System
100,000 (total) pounds
Shirtsleeve environment

LAUNCH VEHICLE: Saturn V, 7,600,000 pounds thrust

MISSION: landing man on moon; lunar orbital and landing

FIRST MANNED FLIGHT: Oct. 11, 1968

Before the Apollo program, man's only method of viewing
the moon's surface directly was through an earth-based
telescope.

The Apollo 10 test mission flew only 10 miles above the surface of the moon. This large crater, 17 miles across, was photographed from 85 miles away.

Significant bonuses should accrue from the technological stretch dictated by Apollo. Technology is simply know-how, the ability of a society to provide itself with the material objects of civilization; it is intellect and skill, new ideas, inventions, materials and processes, all applied to the betterment of human existence. It builds like an inverted pyramid, each level broader than the one below as successive generations make their contributions to the cumulative know-how.

Apollo's tremendous impetus to technological advance stems from the twin factors of breadth and forced acceleration. Breadth, because fulfillment of the commitment required new discoveries not just in aerospace technology but across a wider spectrum that embraced almost every technological discipline. Acceleration, because the pressure of national interest pushed technology through multiple layers of the pyramid, compressing into less than one decade the normal advance of several.

Already hundreds of new products and techniques have emerged as a direct result of Apollo research, but by no means do they represent the payoff from the investment; they are only the first tangible evidence of greater things to come. It is too early for the full impact of Apollo influence, because application of technology traditionally lags behind capability. But, inevitably, a technological thrust of Apollo's dimensions will make its mark on our mode of life, perhaps in some startling transformation we cannot imagine today.

In the sense that enlightenment is a nobler goal than exploitation, the greatest benefits of Apollo may be scientific rather than technological. The moon has long fascinated the scientific community, who feel that it holds many of the keys to the great mystery of the origin of the universe. Earth, until now the only planet science has been able to study at first hand, is continually changing, eroded by wind, waves, rain, and glacier movement. The moon, however, except for the pocking of its surface by cosmic pellets, exists today as it did billions of years ago. It offers an extension of scientific reach into a distant past that long predates humanity; it holds promise of clues that may tell us how and when the solar system was formed.

Was the moon a part of earth, broken off in some prehistoric cataclysm? Or was it an independent planet from some other part of the universe that strayed into earth's gravitational field and was captured? Is there frozen water beneath its surface? Are there lingering traces of a one-time atmosphere which lunar gravity was too weak to hold? What are the rills that look like dried rivers, the rays that fan out from some of the craters? What is the source of the mysterious red glowings noted in recent years? Is the moon really dead, or is there some sort of volcanic action still taking place far beneath its surface? Did any form of life ever exist there? The answers to these and a hundred questions like them are the missing pieces of the jigsaw puzzle; if they can be found and mated with the fragments science has already assembled, a truly broad picture of the universe and its origins will begin to emerge.

Through the combination of instruments deposited directly on the moon, samples brought back to earth for detailed analysis, and the human ability to observe and evaluate, Apollo promises to supply many of the missing jigsaw bits. At the same time, it elevates man to a new plateau of capability for further probing of the eternal enigma. Apollo represents a monumental advance in man's search for his own identity, as valuable a legacy as one generation can pass to another.

The Saturn V Launch Vehicle

CHAPTER 2

IF, AT A GIVEN INSTANT, ALL the moving waters of North America were channeled through turbines and their energy converted to hydroelectric power, the horsepower equivalent thus generated would be only about half that produced by the mighty launch vehicle that starts an Apollo spacecraft on its way to the moon.

That incredible fact is but one of many indications that the development of the Saturn V launch vehicle represents one of the greatest technological achievements of all time. Saturn V is the biggest, the heaviest, and the most powerful flying machine ever built, not because its designers were out to set records but because the extraordinary demands of a manned lunar mission would permit nothing less. Why this is so is a fascinating story, but before going into it, perhaps it would be appropriate to define just what is meant by "launch vehicle." There appears to exist considerable confusion with regard to the terms "space vehicle," "spacecraft," and "launch vehicle," frequently used interchangeably but incorrectly so.

The *space vehicle* is the "whole ball of wax"; also called the *stack*, because it is a stack of separate components, it consists of everything on the launch pad that is intended to fly.

The *spacecraft*, be it manned or unmanned, is that portion of the stack that operates in space.

The *launch vehicle* is that portion of the stack that sends the spacecraft into space.

Naturally, a definition as simple as that cannot be 100 percent correct. In the case of Saturn V there is a hybrid section that is part launch vehicle and part spacecraft, but let's defer discussion of that exception until later.

The job of a launch vehicle is akin to that of a slingshot: it must impart

WHY SATURN V IS SO BIG

LIFTOFF THRUST REQUIRED TO ACHIEVE VARIOUS ORBITS
WITH A 50-TON APOLLO PAYLOAD

Orbital altitude (nautical miles)	100 by 100 (circular)	100 by 1,415 (elliptical)	100 by 3,700	100 by 18,600	100 by 240,000 (lunar distance)
Liftoff thrust required with two stages	4,170,000 lb.	5,550,000 lb.	7,400,000 lb.	16,200,000 lb.	40,000,000 lb.
Liftoff thrust required with three stages	2,400,000 lb.	3,000,000 lb.	3,500,000 lb.	6,100,000 lb.	7,600,000 lb.

(NOTE: a single-stage launch vehicle cannot reach the velocity required to send a payload to the moon.)

velocity to a projectile and direct it toward a target. In the case of the launch vehicle, the target is a point in space and the velocity requirement is in the vicinity of 17,500 miles per hour.

Nature is not very cooperative in the matter of hurling objects into space. It provides two forms of resistance: *gravity* and *atmosphere*. Gravity acts like a very strong chain, exerting a pull toward the center of the earth which tends to restrain the space vehicle. Atmosphere is a thick blanket composed of billions upon billions of air molecules, densely packed in the lower altitudes, thinning out in the upper regions until, at a height of approximately 400,000 feet, the air molecules are so far apart that they can be discounted as a restraining influence. Like tiny fingers, these molecules clutch briefly at the skin of the outbound space vehicle, their combined effort producing a substantial retarding force called *drag*.

The first requisite of the launch vehicle, then, is a method of overcoming the restraints imposed by nature's guardians of the road to space. The method is brute force; the medium is a *propulsion system* composed of one or more engines.

The type of engine employed in the launch vehicle propulsion system is the *rocket,* a close relative of the familiar turbojet. Both types are members

The basic rocket engine burns fuel and an oxidizer to create a thrust which propels the craft forward in reaction. This principle holds true regardless of the size of the engine.

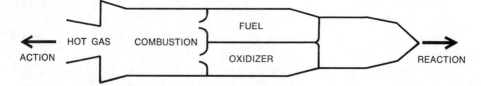

of the *reaction* family: by burning fuel with another substance and expelling the resulting gas rearward at high velocity, they create a reaction which is propulsive force. The difference is that the jet, designed to operate within the atmosphere, uses air as the "other substance;" the rocket, which must operate beyond the limits of atmosphere, requires a substitute for air—an oxidizer—which must be carried along in the launch vehicle. So the second requisite for a launch vehicle is a system of tankage to contain the rocket engine's fuel and oxidizer, which, for Saturn V, is liquid oxygen.

The engines and tanks need protection from damage on the ground and from the forces encountered in flight, so the third of the basic requisites is a cylindrical airframe, or container, with a "thrust structure," a strong base which supports the weight of the launch vehicle and distributes the propulsive "push" of the engines.

Finally, the launch vehicle needs a system of guidance to steer the whole space vehicle to a predetermined point at which the spacecraft enters orbit.

Engines for Thrust

The launch vehicle's first job is to overcome drag, or to drill through the blanket of atmosphere. This is accomplished simply by the application of a *thrust* force—the power of the engines—which is superior to the drag created by the clutching air molecules.

Counteracting gravity is a far more difficult job. The launch vehicle, first of all, must have enough thrust to lift the entire weight of the space vehicle; thrust is measured in pounds, so there must be more than one pound of thrust for each pound of vehicle weight if the stack is to get off the ground. But simply lifting off is not enough; the major requirement for counteracting gravity is a very high velocity. Velocity creates a new force— *centrifugal force*—which opposes gravity by pulling outward.

To put a spacecraft into low-altitude earth orbit—say, 100 to 150 miles high—takes a velocity of just under 5 miles per second, or 17,500 to 18,000 miles per hour. The centrifugal force created by that velocity is exactly equal to earth's gravitational pull; in other words, gravity is pulling the spacecraft toward earth but the opposing force is pulling it away from earth with equal strength. The spacecraft, pawn in nature's tug-of-war, has no option but to remain caught in the orbit into which it was initially directed.

But if the spacecraft loses velocity for any reason—for instance, the deliberate firing of a retrorocket—gravity wins the tug-of-war and pulls the spacecraft earthward in a gradual descending arc. Conversely, if the space-craft gains velocity, gravity is overpowered and the spacecraft "falls away" from earth. That is what happens on a lunar mission. Additional rocket thrust is applied while the spacecraft is in earth orbit. Velocity is boosted from 5 to almost 7 miles a second—close to 25,000 miles per hour—and the added force "stretches" the gravitational chain, permitting the spacecraft to move out to lunar distance.

The acceleration of a space vehicle from zero speed on the launch pad to 5 miles a second within the course of the 10 to 12 minutes it takes to achieve orbit is obviously a task of fantastic magnitude. The launch vehicle is aided somewhat by the fact that its engines burn *propellants*—fuel and oxidizer—rapidly, which brings about a marked decrease in overall vehicle weight. To further ease the job of acceleration, launch vehicle design engineers have adopted an en-route weight reduction technique known as *staging*.

In this design philosophy, the launch vehicle is built in two or more segments called *stages* and each stage is assigned a portion of the acceleration task. For example, the first stage pushes the whole stack to a velocity of 6,000 miles per hour; then, its job completed, it separates from the stack and falls back toward earth. Its departure substantially reduces the weight of the stack, easing the work of the second stage, which accelerates the vehicle to, say, 15,000 miles per hour. When the second stage drops off, the remaining portion of the stack weighs only a fraction of its original launch-pad weight, so the third stage can complete the acceleration to orbital speed with considerably less propulsive effort than was required of the lower stages.

The Saturn V moonbooster employs this three-stage design approach. But what stages! The largest, or basic stage, by itself is as tall as a 14-story building and, when fueled and ready for launch, weighs as much as 15 fully-loaded transatlantic jetliners. The complete, mammoth launch vehicle towers 6 stories higher than the Statue of Liberty and weighs 13 times as much.

How did it get so big? The answer starts with the extraordinary demand for propulsive energy. The amount of energy required of any launch vehicle is dictated by the weight of the spacecraft and the distance it must travel from earth. When the spacecraft is the 50-ton Apollo and the target is the moon, an average 240,000 miles away, the energy demands reach monumental proportions.

Saturn V's propulsive energy producers are two types of rocket engines, both built by Rocketdyne Division of North American Rockwell Corpora-

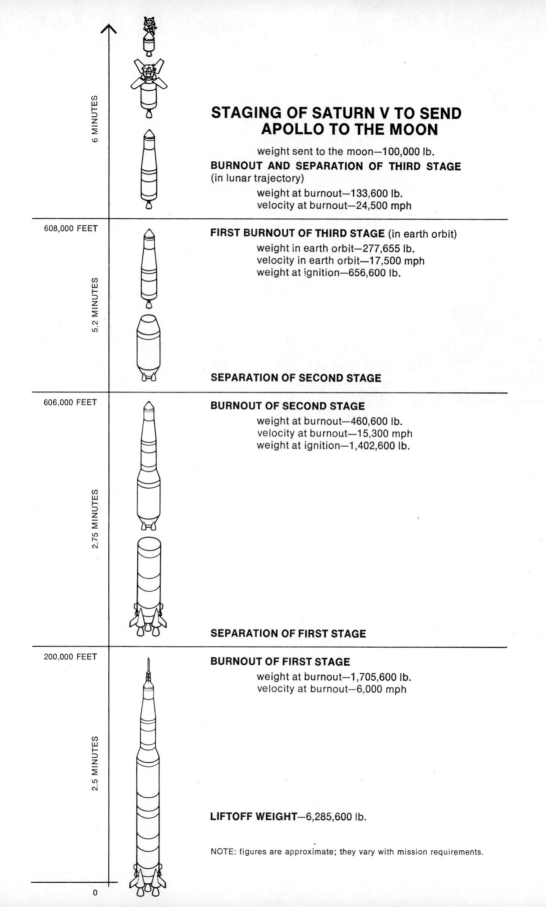

STAGING OF SATURN V TO SEND APOLLO TO THE MOON

weight sent to the moon—100,000 lb.

BURNOUT AND SEPARATION OF THIRD STAGE (in lunar trajectory)

weight at burnout—133,600 lb.
velocity at burnout—24,500 mph

6 MINUTES

608,000 FEET

FIRST BURNOUT OF THIRD STAGE (in earth orbit)

weight in earth orbit—277,655 lb.
velocity in earth orbit—17,500 mph
weight at ignition—656,600 lb.

5.2 MINUTES

SEPARATION OF SECOND STAGE

606,000 FEET

BURNOUT OF SECOND STAGE

weight at burnout—460,600 lb.
velocity at burnout—15,300 mph
weight at ignition—1,402,600 lb.

2.75 MINUTES

SEPARATION OF FIRST STAGE

200,000 FEET

BURNOUT OF FIRST STAGE

weight at burnout—1,705,600 lb.
velocity at burnout—6,000 mph

2.5 MINUTES

LIFTOFF WEIGHT—6,285,600 lb.

NOTE: figures are approximate; they vary with mission requirements.

0

The cluster of five F-1 engines on the first stage of
Saturn V generates 7.6 million pounds thrust and can lift
the 6.5-million-pound loaded Saturn off the pad.

tion, the leader in American rocketry since the start of the Space Age and
builder of most of America's high-thrust rocket systems.

The larger of the two engines and the mightiest in the world is called
the *F-1*. It produces 1,500,000 pounds of thrust in a single chamber, a not-
too-meaningful figure until one considers that it represents roughly 17
times the energy equivalent generated at a given moment by Hoover Dam.

The development of the F-1 engine is most remarkable because it was
based not on today's advanced technological capability but on the technology available in 1959, when the most powerful rocket engine in flight
status was the 120,000-pound-thrust system which propelled the Atlas
ballistic missile.

The United States had not, in 1959, formally committed itself to a
manned lunar landing program. But scientists were thinking in terms of
such a capability. To get it, they estimated, would require a launch vehicle
whose basic stage could generate some 7,500,000 pounds of thrust.

No one seriously considered building a single engine of 7,500,000 pounds
thrust; that was well beyond the limits of then-existing technology. The
alternative, then, was to provide the basic stage with a "cluster" of several
engines whose combined thrust totaled 7,500,000 pounds, for instance, ten

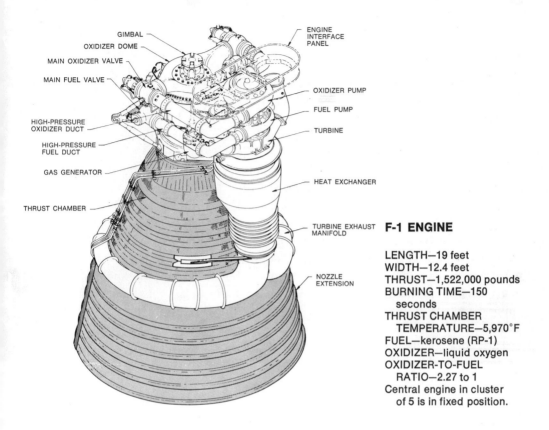

GIMBAL
OXIDIZER DOME
MAIN OXIDIZER VALVE
MAIN FUEL VALVE
HIGH-PRESSURE OXIDIZER DUCT
HIGH-PRESSURE FUEL DUCT
GAS GENERATOR
THRUST CHAMBER

ENGINE INTERFACE PANEL
OXIDIZER PUMP
FUEL PUMP
TURBINE
HEAT EXCHANGER
TURBINE EXHAUST MANIFOLD
NOZZLE EXTENSION

F-1 ENGINE

LENGTH—19 feet
WIDTH—12.4 feet
THRUST—1,522,000 pounds
BURNING TIME—150 seconds
THRUST CHAMBER TEMPERATURE—5,970°F
FUEL—kerosene (RP-1)
OXIDIZER—liquid oxygen
OXIDIZER-TO-FUEL RATIO—2.27 to 1
Central engine in cluster of 5 is in fixed position.

engines of 750,000 pounds thrust each. But the technique of clustering multiple engines is not as simple as it sounds, for each engine requires additional tankage, pumps, valves, and feed lines, all adding to the weight, size, and complexity. In the ensuing battle of compromise, it was decided that the best "trade off" appeared to be five engines, each developing 1,500,000 pounds thrust. This would hold the plumbing at an acceptable level and permit construction of a stage which, though colossal, seemed feasible.

The decision, however, presented an enormous challenge to the engine developers; at a time when a doubling of the maximum power available in a rocket engine would have been a significant achievement, they were asked to provide a twelvefold thrust increase.

Rocketdyne adopted a two-pronged line of approach toward increasing thrust. One method involved scaling up the engine size, expanding in particular the area in which combustion takes place. The other was increasing the pressure under which the propellants—kerosene for fuel and liquid oxygen for oxidizer—are burned in the combustion chamber. These were known methods of uprating engine output, but no one had ever applied them on such a scale.

The developmental problems encountered were massive and too lengthy for listing in anything but an encyclopedia. One example may give an impression of the enormity of the task. To drive the fuel and oxidizer pumps that send the propellants to the combustion chamber under a pressure of almost 1,000 pounds per square inch and at the incredible rate of 40,000 gallons per minute demanded development of a turbine which generates the equivalent of 55,000 horsepower. This is a little more than twice the power of a turbine which drives the largest tanker afloat.

The engine that emerged from several years of painstaking development is as tall as a two-story house, 12 feet across at the base of its bell-like shape, weighing 18,500 pounds. In the combustion chamber, where temperatures reach 6,000 degrees, the F-1 engine burns 3 tons of propellants *every second.* Actually, although 1,500,000 pounds thrust was once considered next to impossible, late models of the engine produce 1,522,000 pounds.

The other engine employed in Saturn V is called the J-2. In some ways, its development represented an even greater challenge than did the massive F-1. Why? Because of the design philosophy of "staging" the launch vehicle. Obviously, if all stages were the same size and weight, the basic stage would never be able to lift the stack off the ground; each upper stage must be progressively smaller and lighter than the one beneath it in the stack.

Initiated in June, 1960, the J-2 was designed from the beginning as an upper-stage engine. Still thinking in terms of a three-stage vehicle that could put a quarter of a million pounds in earth orbit, government planners decided that the upper-stage engine must be able to produce up to 230,000 pounds of thrust. It would have been relatively simple to scale up an existing engine to get that order of power, but scaling up was clearly not the answer for an upper-stage engine; the engine would become so large, its necessary tankage so heavy, that the stage would far exceed the maximum allowable weight.

It was obvious to Rocketdyne engineers that the solution lay in the use of a new type of fuel. As is true with regard to powering the family automobile, different fuels have different energy values. Kerosene was employed in the F-1 and in most of the early rocket engines because it was easy to handle, but it is a relatively low-energy fuel. There existed, in developmental infancy at the time the J-2 program got under way, an attractive substitute: liquid hydrogen. Hydrogen is very light; it weighs only one-eighth as much as kerosene, yet it can produce about 75 percent greater energy for each pound of fuel burned. With the substitution of

About 360 feet off the ground, the roaring F-1 engines
(above) lift the stack past the umbilical tower. The J-2
engines of the second stage *(below)* are seen igniting after
separation from the first stage by cameras which were
ejected and then parachuted back to earth.

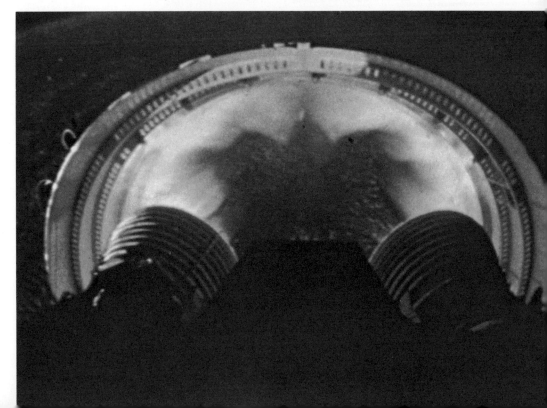

J-2 ENGINE

LENGTH—11 feet 1 inch
WIDTH—6 feet 8½ inches
THRUST—225,000 pounds
BURNING TIME—500
    seconds
THRUST CHAMBER
    TEMPERATURE—5,750°F
FUEL—liquid hydrogen
OXIDIZER—liquid oxygen
OXIDIZER-TO-FUEL
    RATIO—5.5 to 1
Central engine in cluster
    of 5 is in fixed position.
All are capable of restarting
    but only the single
    third-stage engine is
    used for restarting in
    space.

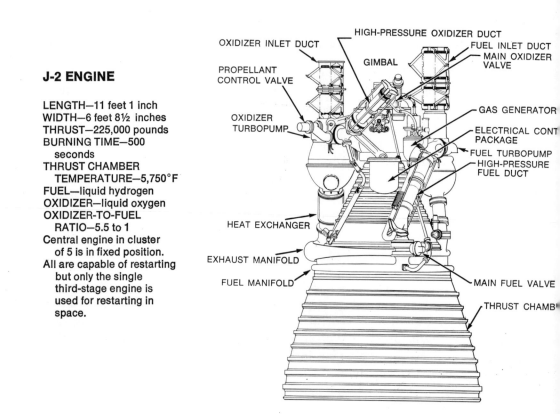

OXIDIZER INLET DUCT
HIGH-PRESSURE OXIDIZER DUCT
FUEL INLET DUCT
MAIN OXIDIZER VALVE
GIMBAL
PROPELLANT CONTROL VALVE
OXIDIZER TURBOPUMP
GAS GENERATOR
ELECTRICAL CONT PACKAGE
FUEL TURBOPUMP
HIGH-PRESSURE FUEL DUCT
HEAT EXCHANGER
EXHAUST MANIFOLD
FUEL MANIFOLD
MAIN FUEL VALVE
THRUST CHAMB

liquid hydrogen for kerosene, it would be possible to get the required thrust from a compact, lightweight engine/tankage system.

The switch to hydrogen, however, entailed enormous developmental problems. Hydrogen is a supercold fuel; it must be maintained at the incredible temperature of 423 degrees below zero. This meant that the development team had to throw away the library of accumulated knowledge of how to build a rocket propulsion system and start fresh. It became necessary to redesign every major component of the system in order to contain the hydrogen at extremely low temperatures, to get it from tank to thrust chamber, to mix it in proper ratio with the oxidizer, and to burn it. Fabrication of each of these components became a separate task of extraordinary proportions.

Somehow—and Rocketdyne engineers still shake their heads ruefully when they recall the myriad problems that bedeviled them—the developers surmounted the difficulties and started delivering engines for ground test within four years of the initial contract award. In February, 1966, the J-2 engine made its first flight, and despite the fact that it was the space debut of a high-thrust hydrogen-fueled system it was a complete success.

Although technically the J-2 is a "small" engine, it is small only in comparison with the F-1; it is the second largest and second most powerful rocket engine employed in U.S. space or missile programs. More than 11 feet tall, it is 6½ feet wide at its exhaust nozzle. It gobbles its propellants at the rate of 11,000 gallons per minute. Unlike earlier engines which burn only once until fuel is expended or cut off, the J-2 can be restarted in space, an important capability for an Apollo lunar mission.

The two great rocket engines and their energy outputs are the primary reasons why the Saturn V vehicle is so enormous. To expand that point, let's take a detailed look at the individual stages.

Saturn's Three Stages

The first stage, or basic stage, is built by The Boeing Company and called the *S-IC*. Its job on a lunar mission is to lift the whole stack off the ground and accelerate it to a speed of 5,400 miles per hour. To do so, the five F-1 engines burn for 2½ minutes. That is a brief period, but remember that *each* engine consumes some 40,000 gallons of propellants a minute.

To feed the mighty engines, the S-IC stage must carry a staggering amount of propellant—the equivalent of the capacity of 54 railroad tank cars. The propellants are contained in two enormous cylindrical tanks mounted one atop the other. Topmost is the *oxidizer tank,* 64 feet tall, which holds 334,500 gallons of liquid oxygen. Below it, separated by an *intertank* structural member, is the *fuel tank,* 43 feet tall and containing 209,000 gallons of kerosene.

Between the fuel tank and the engines at the base of the stage is the *thrust structure,* composed of heavy steel components which provide mounting places for the engines, distribute their power, and support the weight of the entire Saturn V. This thrust structure alone is 20 feet tall and weighs 24 tons.

One engine is mounted below the center of the thrust structure's X-shaped cross-brace; the other four are mounted at the tips of the X. The center engine is held in a fixed position, but the outer engines can be swiveled, or *gimballed.* Gimballing changes the line of thrust, hence the direction of the vehicle, for course corrections during flight. Since the S-IC stage operates in the lower altitudes, where the air is most dense, the outboard engines are covered by cone-shaped fairings which smooth the flow of air over the engines. To each streamlined fairing is attached a large fin for vehicle stability.

Each of the components—oxidizer tank, fuel tank, intertank, and thrust structure—is covered by an aluminum outer skin. Each is of uniform

THE SATURN V/APOLLO STACK

STACK HEIGHT—363 feet (NOTE: some individual stage dimensions overlap, so total height is not the sum of the individual dimensions.)
LIFTOFF WEIGHT—6,500,000 pounds (approx.)

APOLLO SPACECRAFT (3 modules plus launch escape system)

HEIGHT—80 feet
WEIGHT—100,000 pounds

INSTRUMENT UNIT

HEIGHT—36 inches
DIAMETER—260 inches
WEIGHT—4,500 pounds
TASK—guidance and control of
    SATURN V

S-IVB THIRD STAGE

HEIGHT—58 feet 7 inches
DIAMETER—21 feet 8 inches
WEIGHT (dry)—33,600 pounds
(including aft interstage,
7,700 pounds)
PROPULSION—single J-2 engine
THRUST—225,000 pounds
PROPELLANTS: fuel—liquid
hydrogen (69,500 gallons)
oxidizer— liquid oxygen
(20,150 gallons)
BURN TIME—8 minutes (approx.),
includes 2.75 minutes to reach earth orbit and 5.2 minutes to reach escape velocity at translunar injection
VELOCITY INCREASE—from 15,300 mph to 17,500 mph (earth orbit); from 17,500 mph to 24,500 mph (translunar injection)
ALTITUDE AT BURNOUT—115 miles (earth orbit)
TASK—insertion into earth orbit; injection into translunar trajectory

S-II SECOND STAGE

HEIGHT—81 feet 7 inches
DIAMETER—33 feet
WEIGHT (dry)—95,000 pounds
PROPULSION—cluster of 5 J-2
engines
THRUST—more than 1,000,000
pounds
PROPELLANTS: fuel—liquid hydrogen
(260,000 gallons)
oxidizer—liquid oxygen
(83,000 gallons)
BURN TIME—395 seconds
VELOCITY INCREASE—from 6,000 mph to 15,300 mph
ALTITUDE AT BURNOUT—114.5 miles
TASK—velocity and altitude increase

S-IC FIRST STAGE

HEIGHT—138 feet
DIAMETER—33 feet
WEIGHT (dry)—303,000 pounds
PROPULSION—cluster of 5 F-1
engines
THRUST—7,600,000 pounds
PROPELLANTS: fuel—kerosene
(RP-1) (209,000 gallons)
oxidizer—liquid oxygen (334,500 gallons)
BURN TIME—2.5 minutes
VELOCITY INCREASE—from 0 to 6,000 mph
ALTITUDE AT BURNOUT—about 38 miles
TASK—liftoff of entire stack; velocity and altitude increase

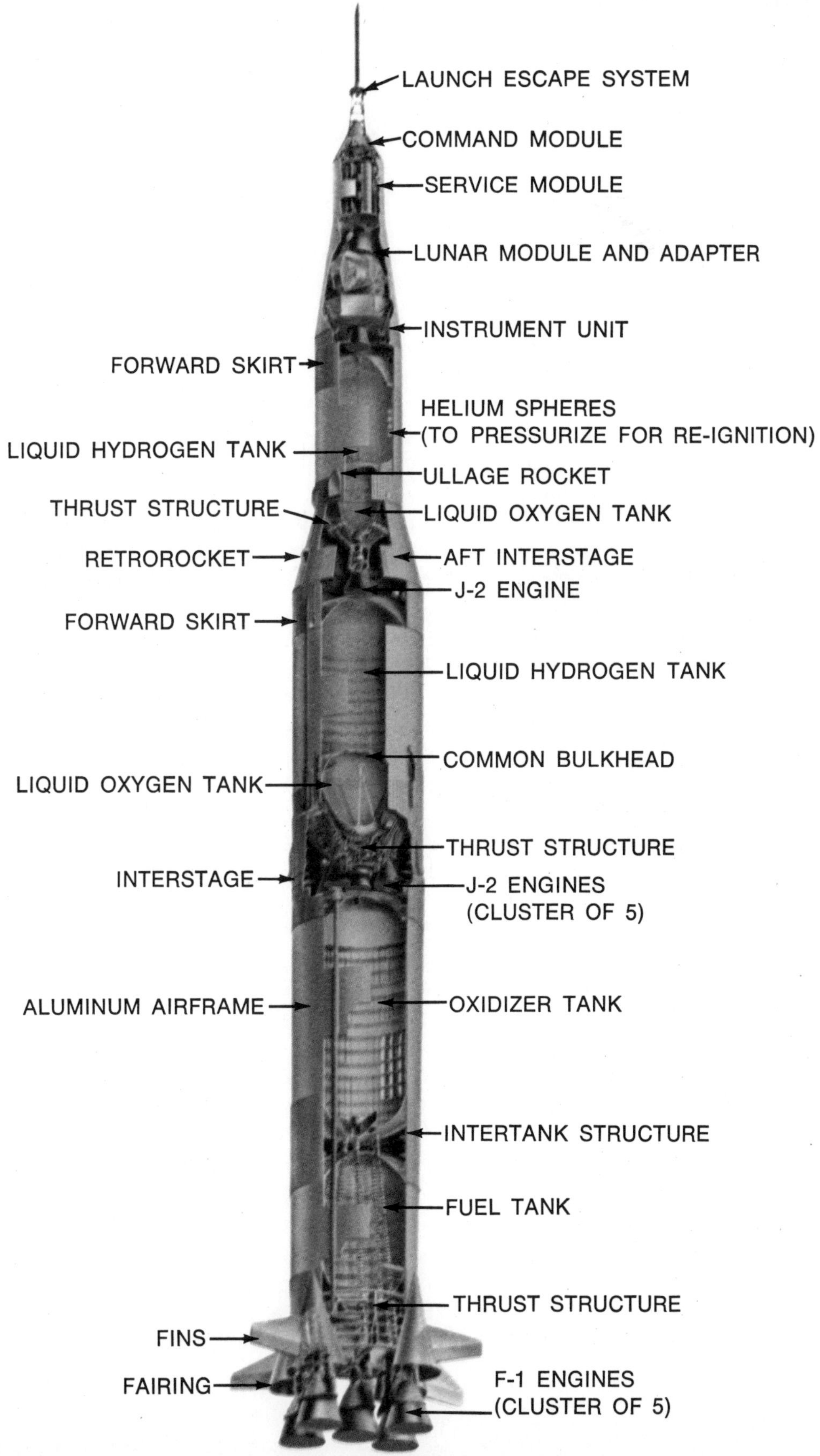

LAUNCH ESCAPE SYSTEM

COMMAND MODULE

SERVICE MODULE

LUNAR MODULE AND ADAPTER

INSTRUMENT UNIT

FORWARD SKIRT

HELIUM SPHERES
(TO PRESSURIZE FOR RE-IGNITION)

LIQUID HYDROGEN TANK

ULLAGE ROCKET

THRUST STRUCTURE

LIQUID OXYGEN TANK

RETROROCKET

AFT INTERSTAGE

J-2 ENGINE

FORWARD SKIRT

LIQUID HYDROGEN TANK

COMMON BULKHEAD

LIQUID OXYGEN TANK

THRUST STRUCTURE

INTERSTAGE

J-2 ENGINES
(CLUSTER OF 5)

ALUMINUM AIRFRAME

OXIDIZER TANK

INTERTANK STRUCTURE

FUEL TANK

THRUST STRUCTURE

FINS

FAIRING

F-1 ENGINES
(CLUSTER OF 5)

diameter—33 feet—so that when they are merged, the components form a cylindrical airframe 33 feet in diameter and 138 feet tall. Fueled and ready for launch, S-IC weighs 4,881,000 pounds; more than 4,500,000 pounds of that weight is in propellants and nearly all of it is consumed in just 150 seconds of flight.

On a lunar mission, S-IC completes its part of the propulsion assignment at an altitude of about 200,000 feet; then it separates and falls back to earth. Separation is accomplished by the automatic detonation of explosive charges. In addition, eight powerful solid-propellant retrorockets of close to 90,000 pounds thrust each, located at the base of the S-IC, fire briefly in reverse direction—upward—to push the depleted stage downwards and clear of the rest of the stack. At this point, the *S-II* second stage takes over.

Built by North American Rockwell Corporation's Space Division, S-II is generally similar to S-IC, except, of course, that it is smaller and considerably lighter. Its major components, from the bottom up, are an *interstage*, a cylindrical ring 18 feet tall which unites the first and second stages during the early phase of the launch, then falls away with the first stage; the five J-2 engines, mounted X-fashion as in the S-IC, but without the fins and fairings; the thrust structure; and the propellant tank.

A unique feature of the S-II is the fact that there is only one tank for the two very different types of propellants; a bulkhead separates the liquid hydrogen fuel and the liquid oxygen oxidizer. This design approach saved an estimated 4 tons of weight and about 10 feet of stage length but, because of the peculiarities of the supercold propellants, it posed a major developmental problem.

Stored in refrigerated tanks prior to fueling of the launch vehicle, liquid hydrogen must be maintained at a temperature of 423 degrees below zero. If the hydrogen warms up just a few degrees, it begins to convert from liquid to gaseous form. Should the conversion reach major proportions, the tank would explode, due to the great pressure of the expanding gas.

Liquid oxygen is also a supercold propellant, but only relatively; it is kept at minus 297 degrees. In other words, it is 126 degrees "warmer" than the liquid hydrogen, and that relative warmth cannot be permitted to penetrate the hydrogen portion of the tank.

The problem was solved by building the dome-shaped bulkhead of two layers of aluminum "honeycomb" with a thick layer of insulating material, in some places almost 5 inches deep, between. This prevents temperature transfer and at the same time affords extreme bulkhead strength, necessary to support the weight of the liquid hydrogen.

Obviously, the outer walls of the tank, exposed to outdoors conditions, need even greater insulation; consider the 500-degree difference between hydrogen's minus 423 degrees and the normal 80-degree temperature at Kennedy Space Center. The outer walls are made of the same honeycomb/insulation sandwich, but for additional protection a second type of insulator is applied. The walls are coated with a foam insulator, applied by a spray-gun like a fire extinguisher. When the foam hardens, it is machine-shaved to the minimum allowable thickness, for while insulation is very important, so is the weight which it adds to the vehicle.

When the various components of the S-II stage are mated, they form a cylinder of the same diameter as the basic stage—33 feet—and 18 feet 7 inches high. Empty, the stage weighs only 95,000 pounds, tribute to ingenious design. Fueled, however, it weighs more than 1,000,000 pounds. Most of the weight is the 83,000 gallons of liquid oxygen; the 260,000 gallons of lightweight hydrogen weigh only 153,000 pounds.

After the basic stage drops off and before S-II's engines ignite, there is a momentary period of coasting flight, and due to the high velocity provided by the booster stage, everything in the remainder of the stack is in partially weightless condition (not complete weightlessness because orbit has not yet been achieved). In this condition, the liquid hydrogen and liquid oxygen tend to float upward, away from the propellant feed lines leading to the engines. Without fuel and oxidizer in the lines, the engines cannot ignite, so the propellants must be coaxed back into the inlets.

For this purpose, the S-II is fitted with eight solid-fueled rockets termed *ullage motors,* each generating 22,500 pounds thrust. As the basic stage separates, these motors fire for 4 seconds. The resultant "push" provides a temporary artificial gravity which causes the propellants to move back toward the inlets.

The five engines of the S-II stage burn for 6 minutes, boosting the stack to near-orbital altitude. Then, like its predecessor, S-II separates with the aid of four retrorockets and starts tumbling toward earth. The job of providing the final increment of speed necessary to achieve orbit falls to the *S-IVB* third stage. With the departure of the two huge lower stages, the assignment has become a lot easier; S-IVB must propel only its own weight and the 100,000 pounds of the Apollo spacecraft.

Consequently, S-IVB is a small stage, if anything in the Saturn V/Apollo stack can properly be termed "small." Actually, S-IVB is as tall as a six-story building and weighs well over a quarter of a million pounds. But for its propulsion job it needs only one J-2 engine instead of the five in S-II.

In some respects, S-IVB is very similar to S-II. Its engine, of course, burns the same types of propellants, which are housed in a single tank

The expended Saturn S-IVB stage, with Lunar Module
Adapter panels open, was photographed from the Apollo 7
craft which used the round white disk as a simulated docking
target during turnaround maneuvers over Sonora, Mexico.

with the separating bulkhead and which demand the same highly efficient insulation. S-IVB also has ullage motors to keep its propellants from sloshing; in this case only two rockets of 6,800 pounds thrust each are needed.

There are, however, major differences aside from size between the two stages and they stem from the fact, mentioned earlier, that there is one segment of Saturn V which is a hybrid, part launch vehicle and part spacecraft.

S-IVB, built by McDonnell Douglas Corporation, is the hybrid. After its initial burn of 2 minutes 45 seconds, which puts the spacecraft in orbit at a speed of about 5 miles per second, S-IVB does not fall back to earth. It has burned only a portion of its propellants, and it has another very important assignment: to aim the Apollo toward the moon and to impart to it the additional velocity it needs to escape orbit and start for the moon.

So S-IVB remains with the spacecraft through one or two revolutions of the earth prior to restarting the J-2 engine for the lunar trajectory "kick." During this 3-hour period, S-IVB must be able to maneuver, in order that it may position Apollo properly for injection into a precise moonbound path. For this purpose, S-IVB has two "auxiliary propulsion modules," located at the base, or as it moves in orbit, the aft end of the stage. These modules contain six small rocket engines, each producing 150 pounds thrust; fired in short bursts, they cause the stage to pitch, roll, or yaw as desired.

Also exclusive to S-IVB is a complex of special equipment necessary to accomplish the restart of the J-2 engine, which sounds like a simple proposition but is, in reality, a difficult and exacting operation. To cite just a couple of a great many technical reasons for the difficulty, the J-2 must be purged of gases left over from the first firing and it must also be reconditioned to become accustomed once again to the supercold characteristics of the liquid hydrogen and liquid oxygen, with which the engine has had no contact for three hours of coasting flight in orbit. There must also be another ullage firing to settle the weightless propellants, but the primary ullage motors have already burned out on the first firing so the assignment is handled by a pair of small rocket thrusters located in the auxiliary propulsion modules. Producing only 70 pounds thrust, these are the smallest of Saturn V's 43 thrust-producing systems used for propulsion, separation, maneuvering, or ullage.

The Instrument Unit, seen being raised for connection to the S-IVB third stage, is 260 inches in diameter and 36 inches high. It is the brains of the Saturn V and contains tracking signals and guidance and control equipment.

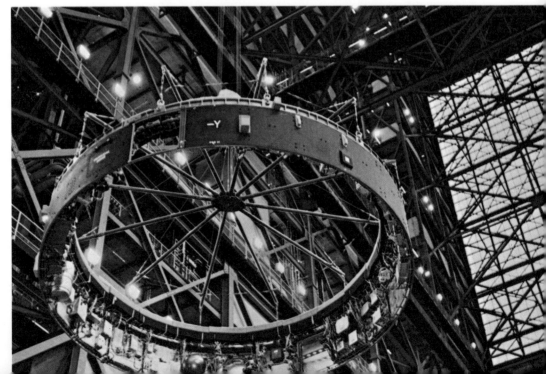

Upon completion of the ullage burn, an automatic device triggers engine ignition and the J-2 burns for about $5^1/4$ minutes, boosting stack velocity to almost 7 miles per second. This completes the work of the S-IVB stage and, aided by four retrorockets, it separates from the moonbound Apollo. Not, however, to fall back to earth; having escaped from earth's gravity, S-IVB is fated to roam in solar orbit, presumably forever.

There is one other segment of Saturn V. It has no propulsion assignment and is not even dignified by the term "stage," but it is a very important member of the team. Built by IBM Federal Systems Division and called the *Instrument Unit,* it is a 3-foot-high ring affixed to the upper, or foremost, end of the S-IVB.

Its interior walls jampacked with electronic black boxes, the Instrument Unit is the robot "crew" of the Saturn V. It handles the navigation and directs the course changes. It is the middle man between the astronauts and the mission control group on the ground, accepting, processing, and passing on information. It keeps a watchful electronic eye on each of the countless systems in the three propulsive stages and reports to earth monitors how they are performing. Sensors scattered throughout the great launch vehicle report any malfunction of equipment to the Instrument Unit, which in turn advises the astronauts by flashing a light on the spacecraft console.

The Instrument Unit's primary job is to steer the giant vehicle into proper parking orbit, then later direct the spacecraft into lunar trajectory. The main components of the navigation system are an inertial platform, a guidance computer, and a separate flight control computer. The *inertial platform* measures every movement of the stack, fore and aft or from side to side, and reports its findings to the guidance computer. The *guidance computer* translates motion into flight-path information—how far the stack has moved and in what direction. The actual path traveled is compared with a "reference trajectory," the desired flight path, which has been programmed into the computer. The guidance computer measures the difference between actual and reference trajectory and passes the information to the *flight control computer.* The latter electronic brain then determines the degree of correction needed to get back on course and signals the gimballing engines in whatever stage is powering the stack to change the thrust line accordingly. This process of comparison and correction is repeated once every two seconds during powered flight until Apollo is en route to the moon. Upon separation of the spacecraft from the third stage, the Instrument Unit remains with S-IVB, to share its lonely, endless tour of the universe.

Such is Saturn V, a monument to U.S. technological capability, whose development took 10 years of painstaking research and test, millions of man-hours and billions of dollars. All for less than 17 minutes of powered flight.

The Basic Spacecraft

CHAPTER 3

A MANNED SPACECRAFT IS A COMPLEX, exotic product of an era of highly advanced technology, seemingly a completely new and mysterious type of vehicle. With familiarity, however, comes the realization that the spacecraft is not all that different from other machines which move above the surface of the earth. It shares with the airplane, for example, a number of common components: a system of propulsion, a means of navigating, a method of control, an artificial environment to protect the occupants, and an airframe encasing the whole.

The modern high-speed airplane and the Apollo spacecraft are lineal descendants of the same ancestor—the first powered flying machine. They are second cousins whose development proceeded along diverging evolutionary paths. The reason for the divergence is air: the airplane flies within earth's atmosphere, the spacecraft operates for the most part in a void where there is no air.

Atmosphere dictates the shape of the airplane; it must be streamlined to counter the drag effect of air. The air is the source of lift which supports the airplane in flight and it is the medium through which control changes are affected. The air provides the oxidizer which makes possible the burning of the fuel in the engine. And it supplies oxygen for heating and cooling and for the pressurized environment needed to sustain life at high altitudes.

Lack of air in the sphere of operation complicates the design of the spacecraft because it must carry an air substitute for use by the propulsion, control, and environmental systems. Airless flight does, however, afford one advantage; designers have great flexibility in shaping the spacecraft, since atmospheric drag and friction are not considerations. This proves

only a partial advantage in manned spacecraft design, since a portion of the vehicle must return to earth through the atmosphere.

The 50-ton Apollo spacecraft, some 48 times as heavy as the Mercury capsule in which American man first entered space, is a masterpiece of efficient design. Technically speaking, Apollo is a spacecraft consisting of three parts, or *modules.* For purposes of simplicity, however, it is better to think of it as two separate spacecraft considerably different in design detail because of their differing assignments. The basic spacecraft is the combined *Command* and *Service Modules,* built by North American Rockwell Corporation's Space Division. The other spacecraft is the *Lunar Module,* fabricated by Grumman Aircraft Engineering Corporation.

The basic spacecraft is shaped like a fat bullet. A conical nose gives way to a stubby cylinder with a bell-shaped engine nozzle protruding beyond its edge. The conical segment is the Command Module, the cylinder is the Service Module.

The Shape of the Command Module

The Command Module, which contains some 2,000,000 separate parts, is the exception to the general rule that spacecraft need no aerodynamic features. The reason is that it *does* operate within the atmosphere, however briefly—about 10 minutes on the way up to orbit and about 15 minutes as it returns to earth. This period spent in the atmosphere represents less than one-fourth of one percent of the average lunar mission duration, but it dictates the shape of the capsule. The Command Module is conical because it is the topmost element of the Saturn V/Apollo stack, the arrowhead, which must have some streamlining to offset air resistance as the vehicle drills through the rind of earth's atmosphere. Re-entry demands the opposite effect; maximum air resistance is desirable for slowing the descending spacecraft, hence the blunt bottom, which is the foremost part of the spacecraft in re-entry attitude.

That blunt bottom is what engineers call a *lifting body.* Although it does not much resemble an airplane wing, it performs a similar function. Angled upward, like a flat stone skipping across a pond, it produces lift as the air strikes the bottom and flows around the upper edge. The astronauts can change the degree of lift, increasing it or "spoiling" it, by using a selected combination of the Command Module's 12 small rocket thrusters to roll the spacecraft.

There are several reasons why it was necessary to provide Apollo with lift and controllability. The primary consideration is the "bounce" which occurs during re-entry. As the spacecraft plunges from thin air into dense air, air resistance creates an upward push which causes the spacecraft to bounce back toward space. Uncorrected, this bounce might shove the Command Module back into orbit—a catastrophe because the Apollo, which has no retrorocket system like earlier spacecraft, would have no means with which to initiate a new descent. By rolling the Command Module to spoil the lift, the astronauts limit the degree of bounce, then gravity starts the capsule on a new downward course.

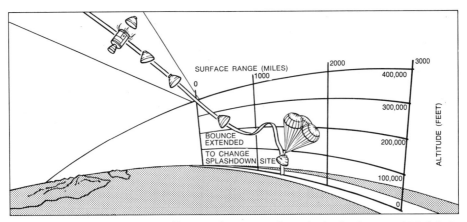

Because the center of gravity in the Command Module is not in the exact center of the craft, the astronauts can use small thrusters to roll the craft during re-entry, to change the aerodynamic lift of the blunt bottom.

Another reason for the lift/controllability provision is the deceleration force encountered by the astronauts as their re-entering spacecraft slows abruptly on contact with the air. Extremely high G, or gravitational, forces could injure the astronauts, but the force of deceleration can be kept within tolerable limits by proper utilization of lift. Similarly, the rate of friction heating on the exterior of the capsule can be reduced by controlling lift.

A final requirement for controllability is the possibility of a last-minute change in landing site on earth. Apollo is aimed at a given site when it departs the moon, at which time it is almost three days from splashdown. Should it later become desirable or necessary to change the splash site for some reason—suddenly developing bad weather, for instance—the astronauts can extend the re-entry path as much as 1,000 miles by changing the lift.

Clearly, a spacecraft subjected to the temperature extremes of the deep-space environment, to the stresses of the atmosphere during launch from earth, to the deceleration forces of re-entry, and to the blast-furnace temperatures of the plunge toward earth, must have an exceptionally strong structure. Yet, like everything else in Apollo, it must be very light, because even the colossal Saturn V can send only 50 tons to the moon.

The Command Module is built like a vacuum bottle, with an inner and an outer shell. The walls are of sandwich-type construction, with a layer of honeycomb material—for both strength and insulation—sandwiched between layers of a special, paper-thin, aluminum alloy which looks remarkably like kitchen foil but is considerably stronger and lighter than any other alloy. This inner shell makes up a *pressure vessel*, an airtight container encasing the crew compartment and its artificial atmosphere.

The outer shell is also fabricated in honeycomb sandwich fashion, but it must be stronger to withstand exposure to the atmosphere, the rigors of space, and the possibility of a meteorite impact. Two thin layers of stainless steel separated by the honeycomb provide a structure which offers roughly the strength of half-inch steel plate at a fraction of the weight.

Strong as it is, however, the outer shell is no match for the searing heat of re-entry. It is a law of celestial mechanics that a spacecraft returning from the moon must re-enter the atmosphere at approximately the speed

The heat shield of ablative material is injected into millions of honeycomb cells *(left)* covering the Command Module. The extra-clean craft *(above)* ready for shipping to Cape Kennedy bears little resemblance to the charred module *(below)* which was recovered and then evaluated. Re-entry heating produces temperatures up to 5,000 degrees F. on the blunt bottom of the craft, but interior temperatures remain comfortable to the astronauts.

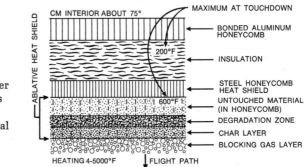

The burning away of the outer layers of the heat shield, plus the effectiveness of the insulation, protect the internal environment of the craft.

it departed earth orbit, close to 25,000 miles per hour or some 7,000 miles per hour faster than a re-entry from earth orbit. Since velocity is the major factor in friction heat build-up, Apollo encounters re-entry temperatures a great deal higher than those of its predecessor spacecraft, Mercury and Gemini. At some points on the blunt surface, the heat level may reach 5,000 degrees Fahrenheit, a temperature which would literally incinerate an unprotected spacecraft.

Protection is provided by a coating, called a *heat shield,* of *ablative* material which is actually allowed to burn off; the burning expends heat energy and dissipates it into the atmosphere. Unlike Gemini and Mercury, in which only the capsule's blunt bottom was heat shielded, the entire outer shell of Apollo's Command Module is coated with the ablative. As it is being applied to the capsule by being injected into fiberglass honeycomb, the gummy phenolic-epoxy ablative material has a consistency somewhat like that of toothpaste. Later, it hardens like plaster, is machine-shaved to the desired thickness, and then given a high polish so that the shiny surface can serve as a reflector for tracking radars on earth.

The process of machine-shaving the ablative is another evidence of the Apollo designers' ingenuity in the war against weight. Early in the program, it was established that it would take 3 inches of ablative coating to protect the Command Module at the point of maximum re-entry heating, which is on the upper edge of the blunt bottom as it meets the atmosphere at an angle. It would have been a relatively simple matter to give the entire capsule a 3-inch coating. But the designers also knew, from Gemini and Mercury experience and other re-entry tests, that the heat distribution over the surface would be very uneven; at the top of the cone, for instance, the temperature would be low enough that only one inch of ablative would provide complete protection. Therefore, they painstakingly computed the temperatures and required coating over every square inch of the Command Module and machine-shaved the surface to the exact requirement, not a millimeter more. From the manufacturing standpoint, this was a horrendous task, but it was well worth the effort. Had the capsule been coated with a uniform 3-inch heat shield, it would have added one ton of unnecessary weight.

Inside the Command Module

The interior of the Command Module is an extraordinarily compact miniature world, which includes, in an area only 11 feet high and slightly wider at the broadest point of the cone, the pressure vessel housing the astronauts, an incredible array of complex systems, and expendable supplies for the moon voyage.

The module is divided into three sections called the *aft, forward,* and *crew* compartments. "Aft" refers to the blunt section of the cone which is on the bottom as the spacecraft rests on the pad prior to launch; Apollo people prefer the terms "aft" and "forward" because, for most of the journey, the nose of the capsule is pointed in the direction of flight. In the aft compartment is a shock-absorbing *attenuation structure,* which cushions the impact of landing on the water by having crushable ribs absorb most of the energy. Also in this section are the tanks for 10 of the 12 small Command Module reaction control engines, or thrusters.

The main features of the forward compartment, the "top" of the cone, are the docking probe which locks together the Command and Lunar Modules, and a hatch through which the astronauts can move from one

The probe of the Command Module pulls the drogue of the Lunar Module into the docking ring. The modules are locked together, forming a tunnel when the equipment is removed.

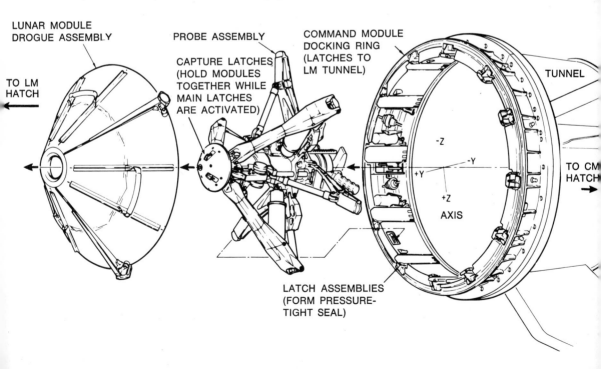

LUNAR MODULE DROGUE ASSEMBLY

PROBE ASSEMBLY

COMMAND MODULE DOCKING RING (LATCHES TO LM TUNNEL)

TUNNEL

CAPTURE LATCHES (HOLD MODULES TOGETHER WHILE MAIN LATCHES ARE ACTIVATED)

TO LM HATCH

TO CM HATCH

-Z

-Y

+Y

+Z

AXIS

LATCH ASSEMBLIES (FORM PRESSURE-TIGHT SEAL)

THE COMMAND AND SERVICE MODULES

LAUNCH ESCAPE SYSTEM

Removes the Command Module containing the astronauts from the launch vehicle in case of an emergency on the pad or during the period before the stack reaches sufficient altitude for the Command Module to separate and re-enter on its own.

LENGTH—38 feet
WEIGHT—8,000 pounds
JETTISON ALTITUDE—295,000 feet
(after ignition of second stage)
PROPULSION—3 solid-fuel rocket motors which, together, are 15½ feet long, 26 inches in diameter and produce 147,000 pounds thrust.

COMMAND MODULE

Serves as the control center and living quarters for a lunar landing mission.
Inhabited by at least one crew member during the entire mission.
Only module to be recovered after a mission.
HEIGHT—10 feet 7 inches
DIAMETER—12 feet 10 inches
WEIGHT (including 3-man crew)—12,200 pounds
HABITABLE VOLUME—210 cubic feet

CABIN PRESSURE—5 pounds per square inch
CABIN TEMPERATURE—75°F
PROPULSION—none (remains attached to Service Module until re-entry)
REACTION CONTROL SYSTEM—12 thrusters of 93 pounds thrust each
RCS HYPERGOLIC PROPELLANTS: fuel—monomethyl hydrazine oxidizer—nitrogen tetroxide

SERVICE MODULE

Contains the main spacecraft propulsion system.
Carries most of the supplies consumed during a mission (oxygen, water, propellants).
Remains attached to the Command Module until it is jettisoned just before re-entry.
HEIGHT—24 feet 9 inches
DIAMETER—12 feet 10 inches
WEIGHT (dry)—10,500 pounds
HABITABLE VOLUME—none
PROPULSION—single Service Propulsion Engine

THRUST—20,500 pounds (in vacuum)
PROPELLANTS: fuel—Aerozine 50 (15,750 pounds)
oxidizer—nitrogen tetroxide (25,200 pounds)
REACTION CONTROL SYSTEM—16 thrusters (in 4 quads) of 100 pounds thrust each
RCS HYPERGOLIC PROPELLANTS: fuel—monomethyl hydrazine oxidizer—nitrogen tetroxide

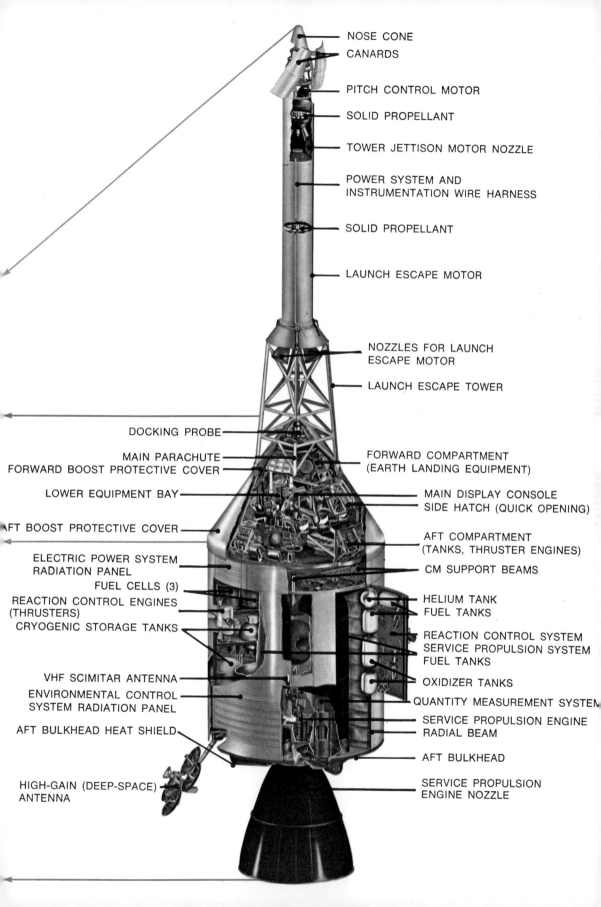

NOSE CONE

CANARDS

PITCH CONTROL MOTOR

SOLID PROPELLANT

TOWER JETTISON MOTOR NOZZLE

POWER SYSTEM AND
INSTRUMENTATION WIRE HARNESS

SOLID PROPELLANT

LAUNCH ESCAPE MOTOR

NOZZLES FOR LAUNCH
ESCAPE MOTOR

LAUNCH ESCAPE TOWER

DOCKING PROBE

FORWARD COMPARTMENT
(EARTH LANDING EQUIPMENT)

MAIN PARACHUTE

FORWARD BOOST PROTECTIVE COVER

MAIN DISPLAY CONSOLE
SIDE HATCH (QUICK OPENING)

LOWER EQUIPMENT BAY

AFT BOOST PROTECTIVE COVER

AFT COMPARTMENT
(TANKS, THRUSTER ENGINES)

ELECTRIC POWER SYSTEM
RADIATION PANEL

CM SUPPORT BEAMS

FUEL CELLS (3)

HELIUM TANK
FUEL TANKS

REACTION CONTROL ENGINES
(THRUSTERS)

CRYOGENIC STORAGE TANKS

REACTION CONTROL SYSTEM
SERVICE PROPULSION SYSTEM
FUEL TANKS

VHF SCIMITAR ANTENNA

OXIDIZER TANKS

ENVIRONMENTAL CONTROL
SYSTEM RADIATION PANEL

QUANTITY MEASUREMENT SYSTEM

AFT BULKHEAD HEAT SHIELD

SERVICE PROPULSION ENGINE
RADIAL BEAM

AFT BULKHEAD

HIGH-GAIN (DEEP-SPACE)
ANTENNA

SERVICE PROPULSION
ENGINE NOZZLE

module to the other. Packed around the hatch are the parachutes that permit slow descent to earth's surface after re-entry. The forward compartment also houses the tanks for the other two Command Module thrusters.

The sealed crew compartment is a model of compactness. It contains the control center, an office, a scientific laboratory, a complete radio/TV broadcasting station, a kitchen complete with water dispenser and a 14-day supply of dehydrated food, two bedrooms, and even a toilet, dignified by the term "waste management system." By earthmen's standards the capsule interior, containing approximately the volume of a large station wagon, is cramped. To an astronaut who has flown in Gemini, however, it is roomy, for the 210 feet of habitable area represents three times the usable space in Gemini, or twice as much for each man.

Around the walls of the crew compartment is a maze of console panels which would bewilder the most experienced airline pilot, together with a series of cupboards containing such items as scientific instruments for experiments, cameras, a tool set, a personal hygiene kit for each astronaut, and a life raft, should an emergency dictate abandoning the spacecraft after splashdown.

Mounted about midway of the compartment's fore-and-aft line are the three specially-designed padded astronaut couches. During launch, the spacesuited astronauts lie on the couches. In space, the couches are adjusted so that the crewmen are sitting upright, facing the display consoles; after the launch phase, they can doff their cumbersome pressure suits in favor of a lightweight flight suit made of nonflammable fiberglass cloth. The center couch has a hinged lower portion which can be folded back, creating a space in which one astronaut can stand erect. This space is also an entryway to the under-couch area where the "bedrooms" are located. The bedrooms are simply shelves beneath the left and right couches which permit two off-duty crewmen to stretch full-length on a sleeping bag. Both couches and sleep stations have restraining straps to keep the weightless astronauts from floating.

In the pressure vessel, the astronauts live in an atmosphere which is not entirely earthlike but a close and comfortable simulation. They breathe pure oxygen, instead of the nitrogen/oxygen mixture we breathe on earth, and the capsule pressure is maintained at 5 pounds per square inch, compared with earth-surface pressure of 14.7 pounds to the square inch. Crew compartment atmosphere is approximately the same as that of a jetliner flying at 27,000 feet.

The Garrett Corporation's AiResearch Manufacturing Division supplies

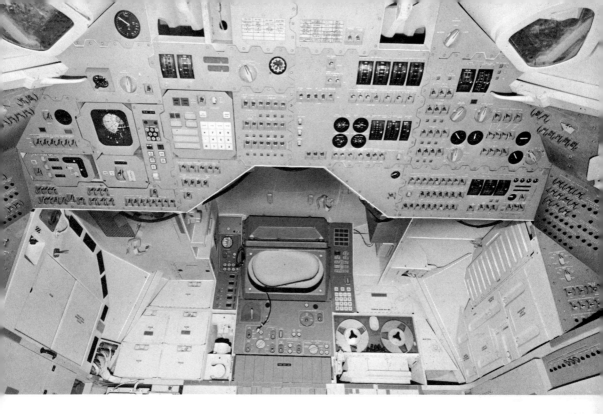

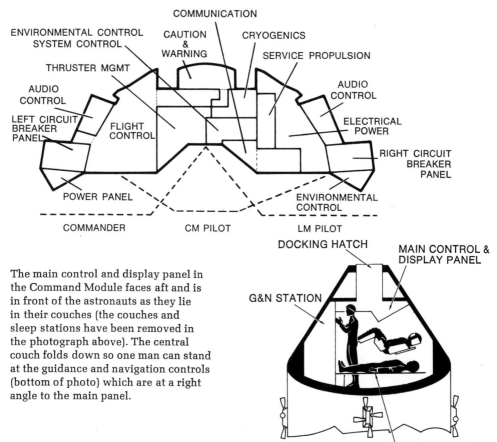

ENVIRONMENTAL CONTROL
SYSTEM CONTROL

COMMUNICATION

CAUTION
&
WARNING

CRYOGENICS

SERVICE PROPULSION

THRUSTER MGMT

AUDIO
CONTROL

AUDIO
CONTROL

LEFT CIRCUIT
BREAKER
PANEL

FLIGHT
CONTROL

ELECTRICAL
POWER

RIGHT CIRCUIT
BREAKER
PANEL

POWER PANEL

ENVIRONMENTAL
CONTROL

COMMANDER

CM PILOT

LM PILOT

DOCKING HATCH

MAIN CONTROL &
DISPLAY PANEL

G&N STATION

SLEEP STATION

The main control and display panel in the Command Module faces aft and is in front of the astronauts as they lie in their couches (the couches and sleep stations have been removed in the photograph above). The central couch folds down so one man can stand at the guidance and navigation controls (bottom of photo) which are at a right angle to the main panel.

Control panel and crew couches viewed through the forward
hatch. The central couch folds for access to the lower bay.

the remarkable *environmental control system* which creates the Apollo
atmosphere and also removes waste products and vents them into space,
eliminates odors and human-exhaled carbon dioxide and keeps capsule
temperature at a standard 75 degrees. A separate subsystem provides the
same conditions for the spacesuits, when they are in use.

In addition, the environmental control system protects the astronauts
against the remote possibility that a meteorite might penetrate the strong
outer shell of the Command Module and puncture the pressure vessel,
causing the pressurization to leak. Should that happen, the system is
capable of automatically detecting the emergency and increasing the pressure to provide a livable atmosphere long enough for the astronauts to
don their spacesuits.

The system is patterned along the same general lines as those employed
in Gemini and Mercury, except that it is a great deal more advanced. It
has to be. Consider the extreme reliability demands on a system which
must operate flawlessly for more than a week in deep space, where no
quick return to earth is possible as it is on earth-orbital missions.

One other of the myriad systems in the Command Module merits particular mention: the *guidance and navigation system*, or the "G & N," as
spacemen term it. This is the spacecraft counterpart of the brainy Instrument Unit in the launch vehicle.

The G & N has three subsystems: an inertial guidance unit, an optical unit, and a computer. The inertial guidance unit senses every fore-and-aft and side-to-side movement of the spacecraft, indicators of how far Apollo has traveled and in what direction. The astronauts use the optical equipment, consisting of a sextant and a telescope, to take sights on the moon, selected stars, and landmarks on earth. Information from both sources is fed into the computer, together with data from earth tracking stations, and the computer continually updates its position in space and reports to the spacecraft navigator. When course corrections are necessary, the G & N determines the steering angle and the thrust requirement. Despite their complexity, each of the units occupies only a single cubic foot of volume.

The Service Module

The Service Module is not habitable; it is simply a support "can," containing a variety of tanks and several major systems too bulky for inclusion in the Command Module. Since it does not return to earth, its exterior has no heat-shielding. The outer walls of the 22-foot-tall cylinder are made of aluminum honeycomb material.

Mounted on the exterior of the can are 16 reaction control engines, or thrusters, each producing 100 pounds of thrust. It is with these engines that the astronauts make all required changes in the attitude of the spacecraft. The space equivalent of an airplane's ailerons and elevators, the thrusters are grouped in "quads," assemblies of four engines whose thrust barrels are aimed up, down, and to either side. With a brief firing of the proper combination of thrusters, the astronauts can position the spacecraft in any desired attitude.

The major, and vital, system in the Service Module is the big spacecraft engine, built by Aerojet-General Corporation, which produces 20,500 pounds of thrust. Officially known as the *Service Propulsion System*, the engine powers all of the course corrections on a lunar mission, including the critical *must* firing that takes Apollo out of moon orbit and starts it earthward. Much of the volume of the Service Module is taken up by the engine's fuel and oxidizer tanks. The propellants are different from those used in the mighty engines of the launch vehicle. The oxidizer is nitrogen tetroxide; the fuel is a blend called aerozine 50. These propellants were selected because they are *hypergolic*, which means simply that they ignite on contact with each other, hence need no complicated ignition system, making for weight-saving and greater reliability.

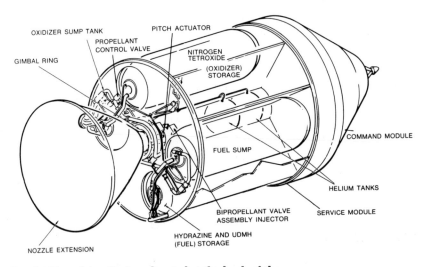

OXIDIZER SUMP TANK   PITCH ACTUATOR
PROPELLANT
CONTROL VALVE   NITROGEN
GIMBAL RING   TETROXIDE
                        (OXIDIZER)
                        STORAGE
                                                        COMMAND MODULE
                        FUEL SUMP
                                                        HELIUM TANKS
                        BIPROPELLANT VALVE   SERVICE MODULE
                        ASSEMBLY INJECTOR
                HYDRAZINE AND UDMH
                (FUEL) STORAGE
NOZZLE EXTENSION

The Service Propulsion System, located at the back of the
Service Module, has the supercritical tasks of braking the
spacecraft for insertion into lunar orbit and of providing
the thrust for the return to earth.

Apollo has a unique power station to meet the heavy demands for
electricity, used for the propulsion, guidance, environmental, and communications systems and their complexes of pumps, coolers, gyros, sensors,
relays, switches, instruments, and the display consoles with their lights,
indicators, buttons, and dials. The Command Module has a set of batteries
for the brief re-entry period when it operates on its own, having cast off
the Service Module. But it would have been impossible to provide, within
weight and space limits, enough battery power to serve the needs of a
week-long lunar mission.

The answer was the *fuel cell* powerplant, a system which creates
electricity through chemical action. Hydrogen and oxygen are combined
in gaseous state in electrified chambers, and the reaction caused by their
intermingling breaks up the gases into water and electricity. The water,
which emerges from the reaction pure and drinkable, is piped through one
of the many umbilical cables which connect equipment in the Command
and Service Modules, into a tank in the astronauts' kitchen. The Service
Module has three of these 44-inch-long fuel cells built by Pratt & Whitney
Aircraft; any two of them can meet the spacecraft's demand for electricity.

The Service Module provides its vital support from the time of launch
until about 10 minutes before re-entry, when it is disengaged to plunge

into the atmosphere and burn up. The question might arise why designers went to the trouble of constructing two separate segments of the basic spacecraft; why not put all the equipment in a single unit? The reason is that the single segment spacecraft would be carrying a lot of dead weight and mass, near-empty tanks and systems not needed for re-entry. This would mean, for one thing, that the parachute landing system would have to have considerably greater canopy area to accommodate the additional weight. More important is the fact that greater weight and mass increases the degree of re-entry heating, dictating thicker ablative coating and adding tons to the overall spacecraft weight.

There is one other component of the basic spacecraft: the *launch escape system*. Mounted atop the Command Module during the launch phase, the system consists of a latticework tower affixed to a cigar-shaped missile containing a powerful rocket motor. Should a serious malfunction of the space vehicle occur during launch, the rocket motor is triggered either by the astronauts or automatically by the Instrument Unit. The rocket spews out 147,000 pounds of thrust for three seconds, enough to propel the Command Module and its human cargo to an altitude over the ocean where the parachute landing system can lower the capsule safely to earth. On a normal mission, the launch escape system remains with the stack for 173 seconds, when the spacecraft is above 140,000 feet and capable of making its own descent if necessary. Then the tower is jettisoned.

The launch escape system is a curious item of equipment. It adds cost and weight to the space vehicle and complicates the arrangement of the elements of the stack. It must be as carefully built and tested as any other system. Yet, hopefully, it is never used.

The Lunar Module 4

CHAPTER

THE LUNAR MODULE, THE THIRD UNIT of the Apollo spacecraft, is unique among manned flying vehicles. It is designed for a maximum operational lifetime of only 48 hours; its sole purpose is to ferry two astronauts from lunar orbit to the surface of the moon and return them to the waiting basic spacecraft. It is fated never to return to earth; part of it remains on the moon, another part is jettisoned in space. And it has no definable shape, although it is sometimes called the "bug" or the "spider" because its squat torso and jointed landing legs suggest a giant insect.

The reason for the odd design is that the Lunar Module is a "true" spacecraft, one which operates only in space and can be built without regard to such aerodynamic considerations as atmospheric drag, buffeting of the structure, or friction heating. Freed of these design constraints, the engineering team was able to arrange the Lunar Module's components in the manner most suitable to working efficiency and the result is the unstreamlined bug configuration.

This welcome design latitude was offset by sharp restrictions in size and weight. One of the most complex machines ever built had to be compacted into dimensions compatible with the Lunar Module's assigned position in the stack and, more importantly, it had to meet a weight limitation dictated by Saturn V's lifting power. Last of the elements of the stack to enter design status, the Lunar Module was allocated roughly one-third of the total payload, or 33,000 earth pounds (everything weighs only one-sixth as much in lunar gravity). Cramming all the necessary equipment into that weight allowance proved a more demanding job than building the equipment itself.

It was weight, in fact, that decided the basic design of the Lunar Module, which has two separable stages. Originally, the moon taxi was envisioned as a single-stage craft, but early computations ruled out that concept. Even a minimal one-piece moon-lander, far less sophisticated than the end product, would have required a high-thrust engine and a heavy load of propellant to effect a departure from the moon, and the taxi's overall weight would have become prohibitive.

But, designers reasoned, since the Lunar Module was to be only a one-time spacecraft anyway, why bring back to orbit all the dead weight that no longer served a useful purpose? Why not return to the rendezvous with the Command Module only the astronauts and the equipment needed to get them there? This would substantially reduce the engine size and propellant requirements for the return-to-orbit flight and, in turn, reduce the amount of fuel needed for the descent because the overall vehicle would be lighter.

So the Lunar Module became a two-stage spacecraft in which each stage has its own propulsion system. The *descent stage,* once its job is done, is uncoupled and left behind on the moon, while the *ascent stage* serves as the ferry to the rendezvous point.

Compared with the rugged Command Module, the structure of the Lunar Module seems rather flimsy. The pressure vessel, or cabin, is made of welded aluminum alloy covered by a three-inch-thick layer of insulating material. But, contrasted to the Command Module's two-layered stainless-steel outer hull, the Lunar Module's exterior skin is a paper-thin wall of aluminum foil through which a fist can be driven. This is entirely adequate protection in the airless environment of the moon.

The Descent Stage

The primary feature of the descent stage is the rocket engine, built by TRW Inc., which produces a maximum of 10,000 pounds of thrust but which can be throttled like a turbojet engine. During the descent to the lunar surface, the astronauts use the throttle to reduce power output and gradually "back down" to the landing zone. Near the surface, they increase the thrust to the point where the "bug" hovers like a helicopter while they inspect the touchdown area.

The engine is mounted in the center of an eight-sided frame which encases a number of equipment bays. The bays contain the engine's propellant tanks and a variety of moon-exploring equipment—still and TV

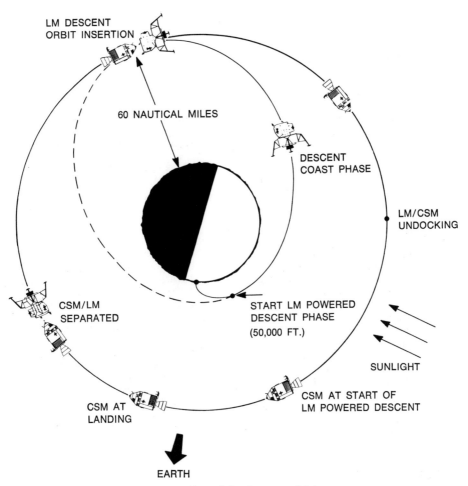

LM DESCENT
ORBIT INSERTION

60 NAUTICAL MILES

DESCENT
COAST PHASE

LM/CSM
UNDOCKING

CSM/LM
SEPARATED

START LM POWERED
DESCENT PHASE
(50,000 FT.)

SUNLIGHT

CSM AT
LANDING

CSM AT START OF
LM POWERED DESCENT

EARTH

After separation from the Command Module, the moonship's
descent engine burns briefly in order to break out of orbit.
It coasts toward the moon until the last 50,000 feet when
landing is controlled by the throttlable engine.

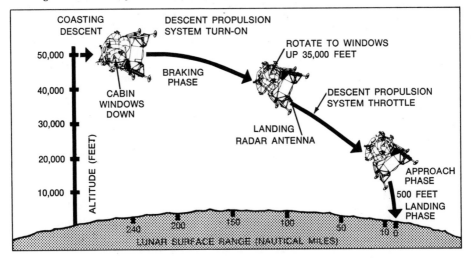

COASTING
DESCENT

DESCENT PROPULSION
SYSTEM TURN-ON

ROTATE TO WINDOWS
UP 35,000 FEET

50,000

BRAKING
PHASE

DESCENT PROPULSION
SYSTEM THROTTLE

40,000

CABIN
WINDOWS
DOWN

30,000

LANDING
RADAR ANTENNA

ALTITUDE (FEET)

20,000

APPROACH
PHASE

10,000

500 FEET
LANDING
PHASE

240   200   150   100   50   10   0

LUNAR SURFACE RANGE (NAUTICAL MILES)

THE LUNAR MODULE

Consists of two parts: the *descent stage*, which makes a controlled landing on the moon and then serves as a launching pad for the *ascent stage*, which contains the crew and carries them back to the Command Module.

HEIGHT—22 feet 11 inches (legs extended)
DIAMETER—31 feet (diagonally across extended legs)
WEIGHT (dry)—9,150 pounds

ASCENT STAGE

Provides a controlled environment for the two-man crew and a tunnel which connects the module to the Command Module for rendezvous.
Jettisoned in space after the crew rejoins the Command Module.

HEIGHT—12 feet 4 inches
DIAMETER—14 feet 1 inch
WEIGHT (dry)—4,850 pounds
HABITABLE VOLUME—160 cubic feet
CABIN PRESSURE—4.8 pounds per square inch
CABIN TEMPERATURE—75°F

PROPULSION—one restartable constant-thrust rocket engine
THRUST—3,500 pounds (in vacuum)
BURN TIME—460 seconds
PROPELLANTS: fuel—Aerozine 50 (2,008 pounds)
oxidizer—nitrogen tetroxide (3,179 pounds)
REACTION CONTROL SYSTEM—16 thrusters of 100 pounds thrust each, firing in short pulses or continuously
RCS PROPELLANTS: fuel—Aerozine 50
oxidizer—nitrogen tetroxide

DESCENT STAGE

Provides controlled landing on the lunar surface.
Supports and serves as a launching platform for the ascent stage.
Carries scientific and communications equipment for use on the moon.
Remains on the moon after liftoff of the ascent stage.

HEIGHT—10 feet 7 inches
DIAMETER—14 feet 1 inch (legs not extended)

WEIGHT (dry)—4,300 pounds
HABITABLE VOLUME—none
PROPULSION—one restartable and throttlable rocket engine
THRUST—1,050 to 9,870 pounds (at full throttle)
BURN TIME—910 seconds
PROPELLANTS: fuel—Aerozine 50 (6,982 pounds)
oxidizer—nitrogen tetroxide (11,067 pounds)

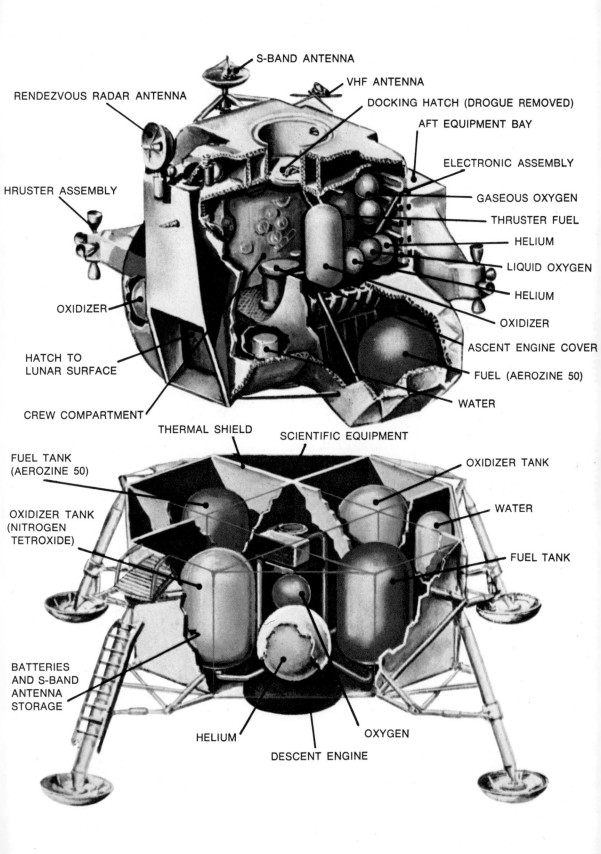

S-BAND ANTENNA

VHF ANTENNA

RENDEZVOUS RADAR ANTENNA

DOCKING HATCH (DROGUE REMOVED)

AFT EQUIPMENT BAY

ELECTRONIC ASSEMBLY

GASEOUS OXYGEN

THRUSTER FUEL

HELIUM

LIQUID OXYGEN

HELIUM

OXIDIZER

ASCENT ENGINE COVER

FUEL (AEROZINE 50)

WATER

HRUSTER ASSEMBLY

OXIDIZER

HATCH TO LUNAR SURFACE

CREW COMPARTMENT

THERMAL SHIELD

SCIENTIFIC EQUIPMENT

FUEL TANK (AEROZINE 50)

OXIDIZER TANK

WATER

OXIDIZER TANK (NITROGEN TETROXIDE)

FUEL TANK

BATTERIES AND S-BAND ANTENNA STORAGE

HELIUM

OXYGEN

DESCENT ENGINE

cameras, an atmosphere analyzer, a seismograph to study subsurface "moonquakes," a device for on-the-spot analysis of rock and soil composition, a pair of containers for the precious moon samples, a surface-temperature sensor, and instruments to measure radiation, magnetic fields, and lunar gravity. Some of this equipment is designed to continue operating and report data to earth after the astronauts leave.

Extending below the frame are the four shock-absorbing landing legs which cushion the impact of touchdown and keep the module erect should it land on an uneven surface. Attached to each leg and stretching about $5\frac{1}{2}$ feet below the footpads is a wire-like probe which makes first contact with the surface. When it does, it triggers a signal light in the cockpit, giving the astronauts a precise fix on height. This is insurance against the possibility that engine blast might kick up a vision-obscuring cloud of moondust in the final portion of the descent.

The Ascent Stage

The ascent stage is larger and considerably more complex because it contains the crew compartment which is the cockpit for flight and the astronauts' shelter during their stay in the alien, forbidding lunar environment. The lower portion of the structure houses the 3,500-pound-thrust ascent engine, built by Bell Aerosystems Company, and its tankage. Mounted in quads at four points on the exterior of the oddly-shaped stage are the 16 rocket thrusters which control the Lunar Module's attitude during landing and rendezvous.

The stage includes an elaborate communications system which enables the astronauts on the moon to maintain contact with the orbiting basic spacecraft and with mission control on earth. The environmental control system is similar to that of the Command Module; its two-day life support capability allows for as much as 35 hours on the lunar surface. The guidance and navigation system operates generally like the one in the basic spacecraft, with the exception that it gets added input from a pair of radars. In the descent phase, the landing radar continually measures altitude, velocity, and the direction to the planned touchdown site and displays its information on a console. For the return flight, the rendezvous radar tells the crewmen the distance and angle to the basic spacecraft with which they must hook up.

With only two men to occupy the 160 cubic feet of space, the crew compartment is slightly roomier than the Command Module. The astronauts fly the craft from two stand-up work positions in front of the

The main instrument panel of the ascent stage of the Lunar
Module is located in the center of the control and display
area. The two astronauts work at the controls standing up,
held against jolts by body restraints.

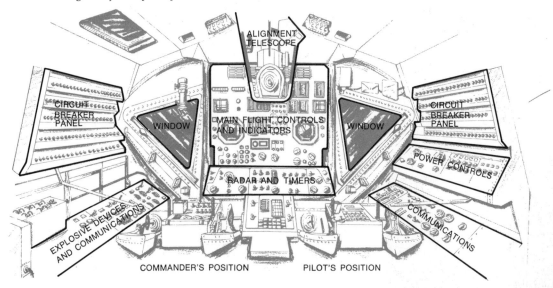

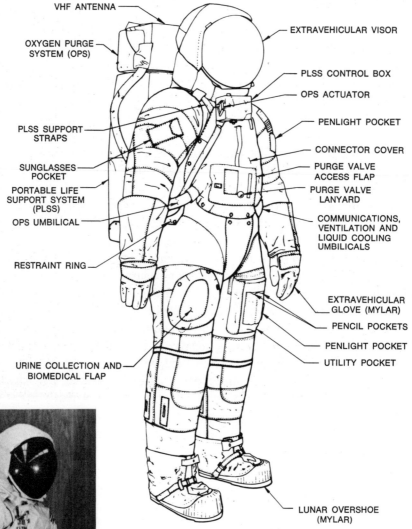

VHF ANTENNA

EXTRAVEHICULAR VISOR

OXYGEN PURGE SYSTEM (OPS)

PLSS CONTROL BOX

OPS ACTUATOR

PENLIGHT POCKET

PLSS SUPPORT STRAPS

CONNECTOR COVER

PURGE VALVE ACCESS FLAP

SUNGLASSES POCKET

PURGE VALVE LANYARD

PORTABLE LIFE SUPPORT SYSTEM (PLSS)

OPS UMBILICAL

COMMUNICATIONS, VENTILATION AND LIQUID COOLING UMBILICALS

RESTRAINT RING

EXTRAVEHICULAR GLOVE (MYLAR)

PENCIL POCKETS

PENLIGHT POCKET

UTILITY POCKET

URINE COLLECTION AND BIOMEDICAL FLAP

LUNAR OVERSHOE (MYLAR)

The thermal garment, stored in the Lunar Module, is donned by a moon-walking astronaut as the top layer of clothing. It protects the man from harmful radiation, heat, and micrometeoroids. The Portable Life Support System on his back, which also contains communications equipment, can operate for four hours without oxygen and water being replaced.

display consoles; there are no couches. Overhead is the circular hatch through which the astronauts enter from the Command Module. Within the hatch is the bowl-shaped drogue, the Lunar Module's portion of the equipment needed for docking with the Command Module. A cylindrical probe mounted in the Command Module's hatch slips through a hole in the drogue as the astronauts jockey the two spacecraft together. It locks onto the drogue, then pulls the drogue—and the whole Lunar Module— some 10 inches until the hatches meet, forming a module-connecting tunnel. Both drogue and probe must be removed and stowed before the astronauts can pass from one module to the other.

To one side and below the work positions is another hatch, a rectangular opening which serves as the doorway to the lunar surface. The hatch opens to a "porch" on one of the landing legs, to which is affixed the ladder by which the astronauts step onto the moon. The ladder is one of a great many examples of weight-saving measures devised by the Lunar Module design team. The extremely thin rungs, intended for use only in the moon's one-sixth gravity, will not support a man's weight on earth.

The ascent stage's "closet" holds special equipment the astronauts need to venture onto the lunar surface, primarily a "thermal garment" worn over the spacesuit for protection from heat, radiation, and meteorite particles, and a portable life-support pack. Built by Hamilton Standard Division of United Aircraft Corporation, the pack is a miniature environmental control system contained in a compact box strapped to the exploring astronaut's back. It generates spacesuit pressure and oxygen for breathing and cools the suit in a lunar daytime environment which might reach 250 degrees Fahrenheit. It also has communications equipment, enabling the outside man to talk to the Command Module or to his partner in the Lunar Module.

The Lunar Module stands 23 feet tall and weighs only 9,000 earth pounds empty; more than 70 percent of its total weight is in propellants. The craft rests in the stack just above the Instrument Unit and below the Service Module. For flight through the atmosphere on the way to space, it is protected by a truncated-cone shroud called the *Lunar Module Adapter* which is attached to the Instrument Unit above the Saturn S-IVB third stage.

Apollo Redundancy and Reliability

When the Lunar Module is mated with its companion modules and the launch escape tower, the complete spacecraft occupies 82 feet of the

On the test flight of Apollo 10, the Lunar Module first flew
in the environment for which it was planned. The ascent
stage, with its two-man crew, separated from the descent
stage at 50,000 feet above the lunar surface and rose to
rendezvous with the orbiting Command Module.

364-foot-high stack. Size is only one of many indicators of the great
technological advance that Apollo represents, but it is a matter of interest that the spacecraft alone is considerably larger than the combined
Mercury-Redstone capsule *and* launch vehicle that sent the first American
into space in 1961.

The key requisite in Apollo design is reliability. The staggering task
assigned the spacecraft demands that all of its countless systems operate
flawlessly for upwards of 200 hours. Along with extraordinary caution
in the manufacture of Apollo's equipment and the most exhaustive agenda
of test and retest in history, reliability is achieved by the design philosophy
of *redundancy*.

Redundancy involves provision of a second way of doing a given job
in case there is a failure of the principal system. With three exceptions,
every major Apollo system has a back-up, in some cases more than one.

The exceptions are the propulsion units—the basic spacecraft's engine and the descent and ascent engines of the Lunar Module. Within weight and volume allowances, there was no way to include redundant engines, but there are duplicate sets of the actuators and valves controlling the flow of propellants to the engines, carefully designed to provide the equivalent of redundant propulsion systems.

Redundancy provisions added considerably to the enormous problems of Apollo design, but there was no alternative. Apollo had to be the most nearly perfect machine ever built by man, more so than an earth-orbiting spacecraft. The craft flying a hundred miles above earth is only 20 minutes from the surface should a malfunction dictate an emergency descent. But Apollo enjoys no such safety margin; at lunar distances it is at least three days from home. Some day there will be rescue vehicles ready to streak to the aid of a crippled spacecraft, but that day will not come within the contemplated span of the Apollo lunar landing program.

The Earth-based Complex 5

CHAPTER

ANY VEHICLE THAT FLIES needs a lot of support from the ground. Poets would have us believe that the airplane is a free thing, soaring birdlike in the heavens, superior to the petty goings-on below, completely divorced from the routine of human existence. A pilot may sometimes get that feeling, but the practical side of him knows that his "bird" flies only as well as its earthbound maintenance men have done their jobs, that a man-monitored network assures his path is clear of other airplanes, that ground radios send the signals by which he navigates, and that voice communication with earthmen is a helpful—frequently vital—factor in the safe conclusion of his flight.

A moonbound spacecraft needs similar support from earth, and, like everything else in the Apollo program, the surface facilities are monumental in scope and complexity. Maintenance, or prelaunch checkout of the several million individual parts in the Saturn V/Apollo vehicle, is a matter occupying the full attention of thousands of people for months before liftoff. Apollo's "control tower" is staffed by a battalion of skilled technicians backed by a battery of supercapable computers which digest and process millions of bits of information every minute of a flight. And the tracking and communications stations which feed the control center girdle the entire globe.

Launch Complex 39, Cape Kennedy

The primary facility is the John F. Kennedy Space Center, the National Aeronautics and Space Administration's portion of the Cape Kennedy installation shared with the military services. The 88,000-acre Center is

The Vertical Assembly Building at Launch Complex 39 is large enough to almost dwarf the Saturn/Apollo stack and its supporting tower as they leave through one of the gigantic doors. The smaller building in the center is the Launch Control Center. The launch pad *(page 65)* is 3½ miles away.

roughly midway along Florida's north-south line, located on Merritt Island, whose northeastern tip stretches to the Atlantic coastline. At this tip, its twin pads only a few hundred yards from the lapping waves, is the Apollo moonport, Launch Complex 39.

Launch Complex 39, which takes up most of the Center's vast acreage, is a sprawling collection of administrative buildings, shops, warehouses, and special test facilities for the hazardous operations involved in checking out the various parts of the stack—high-pressure testing of the environmental control system, the supercold propellants, the fluids in the spacecraft thruster systems (which are potentially dangerous since they ignite on contact with each other), and the solid-fuel rockets which insure stage separation.

Completely dominating the flat landscape is the large, square Vertical Assembly Building. At 525 feet, the VAB is almost as tall as the Washington Monument; it is about 2½ city blocks in length, with egress doors that are individually larger than a football field. In the huge *high bay* area four Saturn V/Apollo stacks can be assembled at the same time. Adjoining it and connected by a wide aisle is a *low bay* area where the stages get a going-over before their transfer to the high bay for mating.

On the ocean side of the big building is the four-story Launch Control Center. This center has four *firing rooms*, each with a massive picture window affording a clear view of the launch site more than 3 miles away.

Here, at row upon row of TV-like screens and flashing-light consoles, the Kennedy Space Center teams conduct the computerized checkout of the space vehicle, the countdown, and the launch.

The various segments of the stack reach the Center by different routes. The mammoth S-IC basic stage, with its 7,500,000 pounds of thrust, cannot be engine-tested in the populated area of New Orleans where it is built at the Michoud Assembly Facility. It is shipped by water, on a specially constructed barge, to NASA's Mississippi Test Facility 45 miles away. The big S-II second stage is also barged to the site from its assembly plant at Seal Beach, California, a 15-day, 4,400-mile trip. After satisfactory firings of the five-engine propulsion systems, the stages are again loaded onto their barges and sent across the Gulf of Mexico, around the tip of Florida and up the east coast to the Center's barge terminal, located close to the Vertical Assembly Building.

The S-IVB stage is small and light enough to fit—just barely—in one of the world's largest airplanes, the Super Guppy operated by Aero Spacelines under NASA contract. S-IVB is flown from its construction base at

The Super Guppy aircraft just barely holds the 59-foot-long S-IVB third stage for shipment to Cape Kennedy. The aircraft, a modified Boeing Stratocruiser, has an inside diameter of 25 feet and can carry 55,000 pounds.

The Saturn S-II second stage arrives at a Cape Kennedy waterway by barge after a two-stage trip from the plant in California where it is assembled.

In the Vertical Assembly Building the Apollo spacecraft, including the Lunar Module and its adapter section, is assembled as a unit and then hoisted to the top of Saturn V.

Huntington Beach, California, to a test facility near Sacramento, California, for engine-firing test, then cross country to Kennedy Space Center.

The Instrument Unit and the three modules of the spacecraft, tested at their manufacturing plants, are flown directly to the Center, the Instrument Unit from Huntsville, Alabama, the Lunar Module from Bethpage, New York, and the Command and Service Modules from Downey, California.

At the Center, each segment is subjected to still another systems scrutiny. Then the process of stack assembly gets under way.

It begins with the placement, in one of the high bays, of the *mobile launcher,* comprised of a heavy steel base and a tower. The base is a two-story structure, roughly square with a half-acre area. The top surface of the base is the platform from which, months later, the Saturn V/Apollo will take off; a 45-foot-square hole through the structure accommodates the rocket exhaust at blastoff. Surrounding the hole in the interior of the base are computers, propellant loading devices, electrical power systems, hydraulic test sets, and a variety of other equipment needed for preflight checkout and launch.

The tower, vastly different from the old gantries, extends upward from one end of the base, stretching 399 feet above the platform floor. A pair of high-speed elevators run through the tower frame, connecting the base and the 18 work levels where technicians perform the tasks which do not require entering the space vehicle. For the jobs which need access to the stack, there are nine "swing arms," enclosed cat-walks which swing out from the tower to connect with entry hatches in the launch vehicle or spacecraft. Propped on extremely strong pedestals, the launcher weighs a staggering 10,500,000 pounds.

The next step in the assembly process is the crane-hoisting of the S-IC basic stage onto the launcher's platform. The engine exhaust nozzles are positioned over the hole in the base and four gigantic hold-down arms mounted on the platform clamp the stage securely to keep the stack from toppling. Then all of the stage's operating systems are hooked up electrically to automatic, computer-directed checkout equipment. In a lengthy series of tests, the computers "ask" a system to perform a given function, "watch" its response, and compare it with pre-programmed information to determine whether the unit is capable of doing its job properly. The results are flashed to the human test monitors, observing on consoles in one of the four firing rooms.

In their turns, the second and third stages and the Instrument Unit are craned onto the stack, checked out individually, then as a complete launch vehicle. The Lunar Module is mounted above the Instrument Unit and covered by the adapter which protects it during launch, then topped by the Service Module, the Command Module, and finally, the launch escape tower. Again, each segment is separately computer-examined, then tested as complete spacecraft. Finally, the huge space vehicle is checked out as an entity, each of the countless systems operating in sequence on a simulated launch. When the inevitable minor malfunctions have been corrected, Saturn V/Apollo is "verified," ready for transfer to the launch pad.

From the spectator standpoint, the transfer is one of the most exciting of the prelaunch operations. An enormous transporter moves into the high bay and under the mobile launcher, which, topped by the unfueled space vehicle, now weighs well over 11,000,000 pounds. By means of hydraulic jacks, the transporter lifts the mobile launcher off the great pedestals that supported it during assembly, trundles it out the door at the unspacelike speed of 1/2 mile per hour, and moves it, via a "crawlerway," the 3 1/2 miles to the pad.

One might wonder why it is necessary to move the giant vehicle; why not erect it right on the launch pad? This, of course, was the procedure for all space vehicles prior to Saturn V/Apollo. It presented few problems in the early days of space research when the vehicles were relatively small and simple. But with each increment of progress, both launch vehicles and spacecraft grew bigger and more complex, increasing the time needed for checkout and countdown. It became clear to NASA planners that outdoor assembly would not do for Saturn V/Apollo. Mating and checkout of the incredibly complex stack would take months, during which time the space vehicle would be exposed to possible storm damage, dust contamination or corrosion from either the air or the salt spray off the Atlantic Ocean. Additionally, prelaunch time would be extended by work days lost to bad weather.

Pad time could not be completely eliminated, because hazardous operations—fueling, for example—must be conducted out of doors. But construction of the environmentally controlled Vertical Assembly Building made possible an appreciable reduction, currently to about eight weeks, eventually to two weeks or less. Had NASA not adopted the mobile launch philosophy, the first Saturn V/Apollo vehicle—Apollo 4 in 1967—would have been exposed on the pad for nine months.

The benefits of mobile launch demanded their price, not only in the cost of the Vertical Assembly Building but also in the expensive and difficult construction of the huge "moving van" and its crawlerway. The transporter posed developmental problems because of the extraordinary

The transporter trundles its 17-million-pound load of mobile launcher and Saturn/Apollo space vehicle up a slight incline and into position over the flame trench of the pad.

Each shoe of the giant tractor-like treads of the transporter weighs a ton and is longer than a man.

weight-lifting demands, but the kinks were ironed out by the time the first Saturn V/Apollo was ready for flight. The monstrous transporter consists of a flat bed which supports the mobile launcher and a heavy steel frame. At each of the four corners of the frame is a double-tracked crawler like the tread of an Army tank; each "shoe" (cross-piece of the tread) of the crawler weighs a ton. The giant treads are driven by 16 electric traction motors, which in turn are powered by two mighty Diesel engines. Even without its great cargo the transporter weighs 6,000,000 pounds.

The crawlerway over which it moves also represents a considerable engineering feat. Resembling and about as wide as an eight-lane super-highway with a grassed median strip, the crawlerway is no ordinary road. It has to support the combined weight of transporter, launcher, and space vehicle—more than 17,000,000 pounds. As a result, it is 7 feet thick, its subsurface composed of several layers of filler, limerock, and gravel.

The transporter trundles its great load up the slight incline to the launch pad, deposits it on the pad, positioning it so that the hole in the base of the launcher is centered over a deep *flame trench*. The flame trench, which bisects the pad, is fitted with a 700,000-pound flame deflector, shaped like an inverted V, which rolls into position directly beneath the exhaust nozzles of the basic stage's engines. Its purpose is to deflect the tremendous sheet of flame that belches from the engines on ignition; the sides of the upside-down V "bounce" the exhaust along the flame trench, directing it horizontally away from the space vehicle. The deflector is cooled by a flood of water and it also has a coating of ablative material like the heat shielding of the Command Module, for a similar purpose: the coating burns off in the heat of the exhaust, dissipating thermal energy, and minimizing pad damage.

The space vehicle in place, the moving van departs the pad on a second haulage assignment. It returns carrying another huge steel tower called the *mobile service structure,* which is jockeyed into position next to the mobile launcher. This new structure has five work platforms offering additional access to the space vehicle for certain specialized jobs such as fueling and arming the solid rocket "ordnance." The upper levels have clamshell-like walls which encase the spacecraft to protect it from weather during the time it is on the pad.

Despite the seemingly endless series of checkouts in the Vertical Assembly Building, another is required when the transfer has been completed. The earlier checks were made with the space vehicle in "dry" condition,

Engineers at the Launch Control Center monitor thousands of prelaunch checkout procedures. Closed-circuit TV cameras and sensors at numerous places on and near the Saturn V and its Apollo spacecraft verify that "all systems are go" as the countdown nears zero.

so there was no opportunity to examine the plumbing for propellant leaks and proper pressures. Now spacecraft and launch vehicle are fully fueled from tanks at the perimeter of the pad, and the stack is given an electronic examination under actual firing conditions. If it passes, the propellants are off-loaded and the tanks purged.

The next to last step in the months-long preparation for launch is a "wet run," with the propellants once more on board. This is a dummy countdown, realistic in every detail except ignition of the engines. On successful completion, the tanks are drained again and the space vehicle is ready for the moon voyage.

The final countdown gets under way 82 hours before launch, as the automatic checkout system begins its electronic inspection of the systems and relays its findings to the launch control center. At ignition minus 18 hours, the propellants are loaded for the last time and the mobile service structure, its job completed, is trucked away to a parking area. The swing arms of the launcher's tower retract, leaving the stack free of all connections except for the four clamps that hold it to the platform.

At ignition, there is a breathless moment when the sheet of exhaust flame darts along the trench but the stack remains motionless. For nine long seconds, the mighty hold-down arms restrain the vehicle while the engines build up power and a computer makes sure they do. The computer surveys the propulsion system's energy output and if one of the five engines fails to reach full thrust, the electronic monitor shuts down all of them and the mission is an abort. If all is "go," the computer sends a signal which snaps back the restraining arms and Apollo is off to the moon.

Houston Manned Spacecraft Center

After liftoff, responsibility for monitoring and supervising the progress of the flight switches to the Mission Control Center at NASA's Manned Spacecraft Center, Houston, Texas. Mission control follows every step of the flight, serves as consultant to the astronauts, advises ways of overcoming unexpected difficulties, makes the major decisions where deviations from the flight plan become necessary, and maintains contact with all of the land, sea, and air supporting elements.

Three major systems serve as the Center's eyes and ears. There is the computer complex, which processes incoming data, compares it with the flight plan, and sends continual updated data on trouble warnings to a battery of manned consoles. For example, one device in the spacecraft continually reports to earth the temperature in the astronauts' cabin. The

Once the launch vehicle is off the pad, monitoring and control
pass to the Mission Control Center in Houston, Texas. In the
Mission Operations Control Room, where communication
with the astronauts originates, controllers watch the TV
broadcast made by the Apollo 8 crew 176,000 miles away.

computer has been programmed to "know" what the temperature should
be at any given time. If the reported temperature does not match the
programmed temperature, the computer instantly flashes a warning to the
flight controllers.

The systems handle as many as 80 billion bits of information in a lunar
mission day. Key to this capability is one of the largest and brainiest
computers in the world. Should trouble develop in the primary computer,
there is a standby ready to go into immediate action, and there is even
a standby for the standby.

There is also a communications, command, and telemetry system, the
pivotal point for information from the outlying tracking stations, which
is similarly relayed to the manned consoles. And there is the voice communication system which permits mission control to talk to the astronauts
or to anyone in the worldwide support network.

The hub of activity at the Center is the Mission Operations Control
Room, with its now-familiar rows of manned consoles and TV-like screens
which display coded information rather than pictures. At the head of the
room is a large, electronically directed map which shows general progress

of the mission, where the consoles deal in more specific information pertinent to the particular jobs of the man watching them.

There are about a score of primary console watchers in the mission control room. To mention a few, there are the director of flight operations, the boss of all phases of the mission; a trio of systems engineers, who keep a watchful eye on the workings of the spacecraft systems by means of telemetry signals processed by the computer; the medical officer, who monitors the physical condition of the crew; the experiments officer, who notes the results of the scientific experiments the astronauts perform; and the network controller, who supervises the operations of the globe-girdling support stations.

The task of the Manned Space Flight Network is to provide tracking and telemetry information to Mission Control, as well as to relay voice communication between earth and the distant spacecraft. In this map of the network, the triangles in circles indicate tracking stations, and A/RIA means Apollo/Range Instrumented Aircraft. The ships placed throughout the oceans are in position to track three events—orbital insertion, translunar injection, or re-entry.

Communications and Tracking

The computers at mission control get most of their input from the Manned Space Flight Network, which includes 14 land stations, four electronically-laden ships which are the seagoing equivalents of land stations, and eight instrumented aircraft. A single station handles both the voice communications and tracking functions.

The stations have 30-foot-diameter paraboloidal, or dish-shaped, antennas, which are adequate for communications and tracking in the near-earth phase of a mission. For deep-space operations, some of the stations have much more powerful 85-foot antennas. The antennas can be pointed directly at the spacecraft for maximum signal strength in the same manner that a rotatable roof antenna brings in the best signal for the home TV. Information as to the precise direction for pointing is provided initially by Houston, then the station "locks on" or "acquires" and continues to follow the spacecraft.

Communications are maintained by the transmission of radio waves at given frequencies, just as they are in earth operation of the air traffic control system. For tracking, the antenna sends out a radar pulse which is reflected by the spacecraft and bounced back to the earth station. The time it takes the signal to make the round trip permits electronic computation of the distance from the station; the direction from station to spacecraft is indicated by the angle at which the antenna points when contact is made. Continual tracking shows the ground station's computing equipment how far the spacecraft moves in a given time—thus its velocity—and in what direction it is moving. All the data are sent to Houston to confirm the navigation fixes obtained by the astronauts from the spacecraft computers and their own optical sightings.

The radio waves by which tracking and communications are accomplished follow a "line of sight;" there must be a straight, unobstructed line between transmitter and receiver. Except in advanced radars in military development, a radio wave cannot bend over the horizon, and this is the reason for the great many stations spaced around the world in the support network.

Apollo operates initially in earth orbit before going into lunar trajectory. It would seem that maintaining contact would be most difficult in the "way out" portion of the flight, but actually earth-orbital flight poses the greater problems. By way of illustration, imagine an observer on the ground watching an airplane in high-speed flight. When the plane buzzes the terrain at very low altitude, the viewer can follow it for only a few seconds. But

Key to deep-space tracking at the Goldstone Tracking Station
in California is the 85-foot paraboloidal antenna *(above)*
which receives signals from Apollo during half of earth's
rotation. The NASA Communications Network *(right)* uses
radio, undersea cables, land lines, numerous receiving
stations, and switching stations, as well as satellites, to
funnel communications into Goddard Space Flight Center.

when the plane is moving at the same speed at high altitude, it is visible
for a long time.

When Apollo zips through space in low-altitude orbit at 17,500 miles
per hour, it dips over a single station's horizon very rapidly; the station
can maintain efficient signal strength for only 10 to 15 minutes. Hence the
strategically spotted stations to permit constant contact; as one station
begins to lose "visibility," the spacecraft is picked up—or "acquired," to
use NASA's term—by the next station along the line of flight.

The four seagoing stations—USNS *Vanguard, Mercury, Redstone,* and
Huntsville—fill in gaps where it was not possible to build land stations,
in the Atlantic, Pacific, and Indian Oceans. The eight aircraft in the network
are extra gap-fillers, capable of being shifted rapidly to areas where

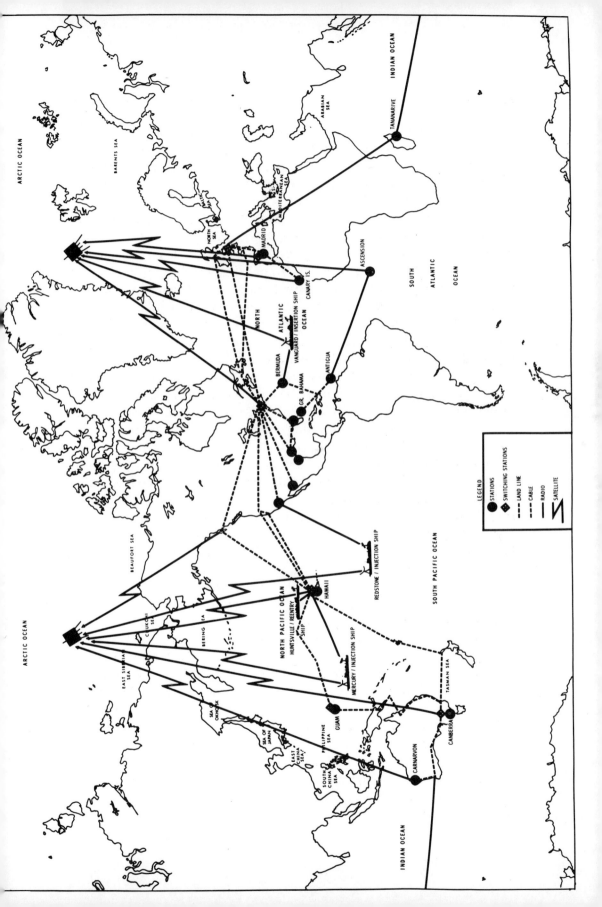

ground and ship stations cannot provide maximum contact. Called A/RIA for Apollo/Range Instrumented Aircraft, they are long-duration jet transports modified to carry a powerful radar, a 7-foot antenna which does the job of its earth-based counterparts, and tons of associated equipment.

As Saturn V/Apollo thunders off the launch pad, it is first tracked by the Merritt Island Station at Cape Kennedy. Which stations go into operation after that depends on the "launch azimuth," the angle from true north at which the stack is launched. For example, a launch azimuth of 70 degrees would take the spacecraft almost directly over Bermuda, so the Bermuda station would take over from Merritt Island. Next, in turn, would come the *Vanguard* tracking ship positioned in mid-Atlantic; Canary Island, off the coast of Africa; one of the ARIAs on station above the Indian Ocean; and Carnarvon, on the west coast of Australia. In the latter half of the revolution, Hawaii would acquire the spacecraft, followed by the *Redstone,* Guaymas (Mexico), Corpus Christi (Texas), and, finally, Merritt Island again. For different launch azimuths there are, in addition to the other ships and aircraft, stations at Grand Bahama Island, Antigua in the Caribbean, Ascension Island in the South Atlantic, Madrid (Spain), Canberra (Australia), Guam, and Goldstone (California).

These stations use their 30-foot antennas to keep track of Apollo until the spacecraft is about 20,000 miles from earth en route to the moon, then a different situation obtains. From that distance, the astronauts can see roughly half the earth, so an earth station on the visible half can also "see" the spacecraft. Except for the periods when it is behind the moon in lunar orbit, the spacecraft remains visible throughout the flight. It would be possible to employ a single station for the entire tracking job were it not for the fact that the earth is turning, rotating about its polar axis once every 24 hours, so in a sense it is the tracking station that moves over the horizon rather than the spacecraft. Therefore, a given station is in line-of-sight with the spacecraft only about half the time, so at least two stations are needed for uninterrupted contact. Actually, NASA has three, to provide some overlap and best signal strength. Equipped with the 85-foot deep-space antennas, they are located at Goldstone, Madrid, and Canberra.

From all these stations, a continuous flow of voice communications and coded data is routed to Houston by every conceivable means—land lines, cables, radio, and communications satellites. Not directly to Houston, however. At Goddard Space Flight Center, Greenbelt, Maryland, NASA maintains the world's largest switchboard. The information goes first to Goddard, where it is processed and relayed to Houston via more than 200 landline circuits.

Navy units provide aircraft carriers and helicopters to recover astronauts and spacecraft after splashdown. While flotation collars were attached to Apollo 10, Astronaut Eugene Cernan was hoisted up to a helicopter for transfer to the waiting USS *Princeton,* in the background.

An example of the effectiveness of the global system is this: A device in the spacecraft relays an item of information to earth. It is received by the station at Carnarvon, Australia, which relays it to a communications satellite in stationary orbit more than 22,000 miles above the Pacific Ocean. The satellite retransmits the signal to a radio station in British Columbia on Canada's west coast. From that point the message proceeds over land lines to Goddard, then to Houston, and it appears on the display board in mission control only six seconds from the time it left the spacecraft.

Working in conjunction with the Manned Space Flight Network is

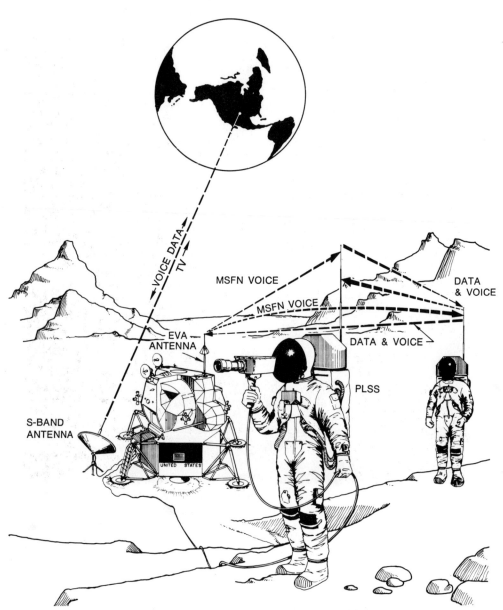

During a walk on the moon, the astronauts are in voice communication with each other by transceivers in their PLSS backpacks. Their signals to earth are relayed by the EVA (extravehicular) antenna on the Lunar Module to or from the Manned Space Flight Network (MSFN). If conditions require, an S-band (a certain range of radio frequencies) antenna can be positioned outside the module for greater signal strength. Communication with the Command Module must go to earth and back to the moon, with a time lag of 2.6 seconds.

another globe-spanning complex which puts space science to work providing extra protection for the astronauts against solar radiation.

Normally, radiation is not a problem. The double walls of the Command Module prevent all but a very small amount of radiation from entering the crew cabin; in the earth-girdling Van Allen radiation belts and in lunar space, the astronauts are exposed to no more radiation than that of a chest X-ray.

There exists, however, the possibility of a solar flare, a sunstorm which spews out high-intensity radiation for millions of miles. A series of Pioneer spacecraft operating in solar orbit send back data enabling scientists to predict the onset of a solar flare before a launch. However, against the chance that an unpredicted flare might occur after launch, NASA maintains SPAN, the Solar Particle Alert Network.

SPAN facilities around the world, tied into the communications network, operate both optical and radio telescopes to monitor solar phenomena. If SPAN detects a potentially dangerous flare building up, it notifies mission control in Houston, which might order the astronauts back to earth. If the spacecraft is too far out to return quickly, spacecraft attitude can be adjusted for additional protection; Apollo can be pointed away from the sun so that its big Service Module is between the flare and the astronauts, providing an additional metal barrier to radiation.

Finally, there is the Department of Defense contribution to Apollo support, the recovery forces. The Navy spots a primary recovery ship—an aircraft carrier with both helicopters and fixed-wing aircraft—near the planned splashdown site. There are a number of back-up ships in other areas, in case the astronauts miss the landing target or elect to change it. For further insurance, a number of Air Force search/rescue planes are on alert status around the world. A similar flotilla of ships, together with helicopters and aircraft, is on station in the Atlantic in the event of abort during the launch phase.

There is no firm figure as to how many people are involved in Apollo support operations, probably because there are so many different agencies involved—NASA, other government agencies, contractors, and the military services. At a conservative estimate, however, it appears that there are about 25,000 persons directly engaged in mission support, not counting the 350,000 people who played a part in providing Apollo hardware. It has become a cliché, but when a returning astronaut says, "It was a team effort," he means it.

Samples of the Moon

CHAPTER 6

FROM THE SCIENTIFIC STANDPOINT, the most important element of NASA's ground complex is a facility which plays no direct part in Apollo flight operations but becomes the focal point when the astronauts return to earth. It is the Lunar Receiving Laboratory at Houston, where the incalculably valuable samples brought back from the moon undergo their initial scrutiny.

The laboratory represents an investment of more than $8,000,000, largely required by the elaborate anti-contamination precautions. The lunar rocks and soil brought back by the astronauts must not be exposed to any type of earth influence which might cause deterioration of the samples and destroy their scientific value. At the same time, the laboratory's design must protect earth's peoples against the possibility of bacterial contamination from the moon. This, most scientists feel, is an unlikely eventuality; all the evidence indicates that the moon is incapable of supporting even microorganisms. But, until that becomes scientific fact rather than theory, the moon samples must be approached with caution.

The Lunar Receiving Laboratory is completely sealed off from the outside world, except for administrative offices and areas such as the visitors' viewing room, where Apollo ground teams can "debrief" the astronauts through glass partitions. Air pressure within the lab is kept lower than that of the outside air so that, in the remote chance of a leak in the "biological barrier," the air would flow inward rather than outward. The air conditioning system has superefficient filters that stop the passage of any type of germs, and everything entering or leaving the isolated area goes through air locks sterilized by ultraviolet light. Returning moonmen

The samples of moon rock and dust which the astronauts
bring back are vital for an understanding of earth's satellite.
Astronauts Edwin Aldrin *(left)* and Neil Armstrong *(right)*
rehearse the techniques of lunar sampling for the Apollo 11
lunar landing when they searched for a variety of different
kinds of rock to return to waiting scientists.

In a shipboard test of procedures for astronauts returning from the moon, an Apollo spacecraft is joined to the Mobile Quarantine Facility by a sterile tunnel. Astronauts remain isolated in the facility from the time of their arrival aboard ship until delivered to the Lunar Receiving Laboratory.

must spend at least three weeks in their sealed quarters, while lunar samples are quarantined for a minimum of 30 days.

The anti-contamination process begins before an Apollo mission when the two containers for the moon samples are "degassed," or vacuumized. Then they are triple-sealed to prevent entry, during the trip to the moon, of any gases from the spacecraft's environmental control system. The containers are opened only in the natural vacuum of the moon, and even then the astronauts take them some distance from the Lunar Module to reduce the possibility of contamination by traces of rocket exhaust. Scientists want to be very sure that the rock samples show only lunar characteristics.

The astronauts are extremely careful in the selection of samples; they do not want just any rocks, but certain types of specimens. They know what to look for because all moon explorers are trained geologists; they have spent hundreds of training hours in the classroom and made a number of field trips to places such as the Grand Canyon, Arizona's Meteor Crater, the Alaskan tundra, and the wastelands of Iceland, learning to distinguish a variety of rock and soil types.

Using special tools for chipping, digging, and scraping, the astronauts pick a cross-section of lunar samples calculated to produce maximum scientific value. Each specimen is placed in a plastic bag and tagged as to time and location of its discovery. Then the containers, each of which holds up to 50 pounds of moonrock, are again sealed.

Once aboard the recovery carrier after the return flight and splashdown, astronauts and samples enter a presterilized, trailer-like Mobile Quarantine Facility, in which they are flown to Houston in complete isolation.

Bits of the Moon on Earth

While the astronauts begin a lengthy series of biomedical examinations in one part of the Lunar Receiving Laboratory, science's long-awaited look at the lunar samples takes place in an adjacent area. Sprayed to eliminate any possible exterior bacteria, the "rock boxes" are placed in glassed-in vacuum chambers, where technicians can handle the samples by means of thick rubber gloves inserted through airtight ports.

The first test involves plunging a thin tube into an opening in each container. The tube captures any gas trapped in the boxes and directs it to a device which analyzes the chemical make-up of gases.

Then the containers are opened. Each sample is extracted, weighed, measured, microscope-viewed, and still-photographed, while a TV system records the whole process.

Initial sample examinations embrace "time-dependent" studies, those which must be made as soon as possible after the containers are opened. An example is the determination of radioactivity, which might fade to a false reading were the radiation count delayed. In order to reduce normal background radiation to the greatest possible extent, radioactivity testing is conducted in a chamber located 50 feet underground and built of materials with very low radioactivity levels.

Next, chippings from each of the samples are distributed to specialized laboratories within the isolated area of the Houston complex. Some, for instance, go to the physical/chemical laboratory, where they are exposed to various gases and observed for reaction and analyzed for mineral and chemical content.

Other chips go to the biological laboratory where researchers look for the existence of life forms by putting the samples in contact with a great variety of earth's living organisms, such as plants, tissue, eggs, insects, fish, birds, and land animals. In a typical test, white mice are exposed to the moon specimens. These mice have lived their entire lives in an absolutely

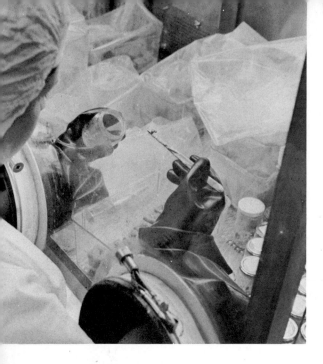

A laboratory technician at the Lunar Receiving Laboratory works with one of more than 20 types of plants which are used in biological tests of moonrock.

The Early Apollo Scientific Experiments Payload was left on the moon by the lunar landing astronauts. It contains three experiments: a passive seismometer *(right)* to detect motions of the lunar crust, a laser ranging retro-reflector *(far right)* to serve as a target for earth-based laser measurements of the earth and moon, and solar wind analysis equipment.

sterile environment free from any kind of earth contamination. If they develop adverse symptoms, the lunar material is suspect.

These and a great many similar tests constitute the preliminary examination phase, the aim of which is to develop a general understanding of the characteristics of each lunar sample as a basis for further research. At the end of the quarantine period, NASA's Preliminary Examination Team sorts out the samples, classifies them, compiles a catalog, and prepares specimens for more detailed evaluation by some 140 carefully selected scientific specialists known as Principal Investigators.

Depending upon his specialty and the type of advanced testing to be conducted, a Principal Investigator receives a sample which might range from a complete rock to a barely visible chipping the size of a grain of sand. To each specimen is appended its history, including the tests conducted on similar samples at Houston. Working in their own laboratories around the country, the Principal Investigators perform a broad range of experiments with the moon material, covering four general areas: analysis of biochemical/organic, mineral, chemical/isotopic, and physical properties. Their work completed, the investigators meet with each other and with NASA's staff to compare notes, while what is left of the samples is passed on to secondary researchers for another round of experiments. A few pounds of rock can be made to stretch a long, long way.

Assuming extended government funding of the lunar landing program, the examination of lunar specimens will be a continuous process. From each successive Apollo mission, the research teams will acquire a new batch of moon materials, potentially different from earlier samples because

they are obtained from different moon locales. More investigators will be invited to participate, and additional tests will be devised as the initial effort suggests new approaches.

It is not expected that any single experiment will yield some sweeping discovery of staggering dimension. Rather, from thousands of individual tests there will emerge, bit by bit, new volumes of scientific information. From a few boxes of moonstuff, man may soon be able to make a conclusive assessment of earth/moon beginnings, keys to the broader mystery of the origin of the universe.

Apollo's Pathfinders 7

CHAPTER

FOR SOME FOUR AND A HALF BILLION YEARS, the airless, sound-less moon existed in near-pristine state, its surface only occasionally disturbed by the cratering impact of a meteor.

But in 1959 the moon was first pocked by a man-made object, and over the next decade the surface was subjected to a barrage of unmanned space-craft visitations. By the time Apollo 8 made its epochal journey at the end of 1968, the moonscape was dotted by more than a score of robot carcasses, monuments to an intensified period of lunar research during which man learned more about the ancient satellite than in all the preceding years of history.

Most of these unmanned moon-explorers were American spacecraft of three types: Ranger, Surveyor, and Lunar Orbiter, Apollo's pathfinders. They were necessary because earth-based observations were inadequate to the tasks of determining whether manned landings were feasible and of selecting touchdown sites from the dual standpoint of astronaut safety and maximum scientific benefit. Even the most powerful telescopic cameras offered insufficient "resolution," the degree of accuracy with which a photo-interpreter can distinguish physical features, calculate their size, and measure the distance between objects.

The Hard-landing Rangers

First of the U.S. mooncraft was Ranger. Ranger was a "hard-lander," a euphemistic term which means simply that it was designed to crash on the lunar surface. The spacecraft's payload consisted of six television cameras which continually relayed photos to earth throughout the last thousand

Before scientists could select landing sites where astronauts could safely land, the moon had to be thoroughly mapped. Photographs such as this close-up of Tycho Crater were relayed to earth by telemetry signals from three series of pathfinding unmanned spacecraft.

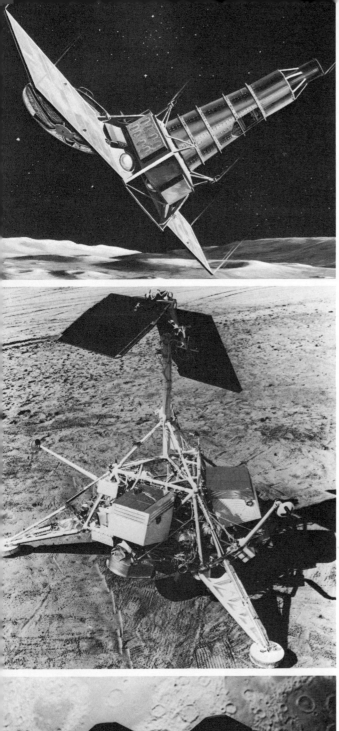

RANGER

MISSION—photographic; hard-
    landing to test lunar surface
LAUNCH VEHICLE—Atlas-Agena
FIRST FLIGHT—8/23/61
LAST FLIGHT—3/21/65
RECORD—3 successes; 6 failures;
    17,259 close-up photos returned

SURVEYOR

MISSION—photographic; soft-
    landing to test lunar surface
LAUNCH VEHICLE—Atlas-Centaur
FIRST FLIGHT—5/30/66
LAST FLIGHT—1/6/68
RECORD—5 successes; 2 failures;
    86,000 photos returned; chemical
    and physical analysis of surface
    material

LUNAR ORBITER

MISSION—photographic;
    measurement of radiation and
    micrometeoroids in lunar region
LAUNCH VEHICLE—Atlas-Agena D
FIRST FLIGHT—8/10/66
LAST FLIGHT—8/1/67
RECORD—5 successes in 5 launches;
    1,000 close-up photos of potential
    Apollo landing sites returned

miles of flight as the vehicle hurtled moonward at about 5,000 miles per hour.

Ranger entered flight status late in 1961 but for a long time thereafter it looked as though the basic question of whether the lunar surface would permit a manned landing might go unanswered. Although two of the first six spacecraft managed to reach the moon, all six missions were photographic failures. Then, in July, 1964, Ranger 7 flew a perfect trajectory and crashed squarely on its target, the lunar *mare* known as the Sea of Clouds. For 17 minutes before impact the cameras returned more than 4,000 pictures with resolutions more than a thousand times better than any ever made by earth-based telescopes; photos taken during the last seconds of flight showed details measurable in inches.

Rangers 8 and 9, flown the following year to targets in the Sea of Tranquillity and the great crater Alphonsus, were similarly successful. In all, Ranger provided more than 17,000 photos and uncovered a variety of lunar topographical features never before seen by man. The program answered the big question: there *were* flat areas sufficiently large to allow safe manned landings.

Though its contribution was invaluable, Ranger had photographed only three general areas from varying altitudes. For selection of manned landing sites, NASA needed a great deal more information. The space agency had to research the possibility, advanced by some scientists, that the lunar surface was a sea of very fine dust into which a landing spacecraft would sink. There was also a need for close-up surface pictures of even sharper detail than Ranger had provided. And there was a requirement for a complete, high-resolution lunar atlas, a photo-mapping of every inch of the moon in order to identify the most promising landing sites and the approaches to them. These jobs fell to Surveyor and Lunar Orbiter.

The Moon Mappers

Surveyor was a soft-landing spacecraft capable of dropping gently to the lunar surface and relaying minutely detailed photos of the lunar topography. It was equipped with a single TV camera coupled with a rotating mirror that could turn through a complete circle; the camera photographed the mirror image and directed back to earth stations a view roughly equivalent to that of a man standing on the moon and shifting his gaze to every point of the compass. Surveyor also carried scientific instruments, a device for chemical analysis of the lunar soil and another for measurement of the "surface bearing," or the degree to which the surface can support weight.

Potential Apollo landing sites were selected from photographs pieced together to show large areas. Lunar Orbiter III made the mosaic picture of Site 4 (*on map at right*) in the Ocean of Storms. The initial five sites are all located in the equatorial region of the moon.

Between May, 1966, and January, 1968, NASA conducted seven Surveyor missions. Two of them failed, but the five successes accumulated more than 86,000 close-up pictures. Surveyor also settled the surface-bearing issue. There was a layer of dust on the moon, the spacecraft reported, but it demonstrated by photographing its own footpads that a vehicle weighing 600 earth-pounds at touchdown would dent the moonsoil only an inch or so. Program results indicated that the surface has roughly the consistency of wet sand, more than adequate for a landing by a manned Lunar Module.

Lunar Orbiter was not a lander; it reached the moon only after concluding its mission, when it was deliberately crashed. Equipped with a dual-lens camera of extremely high resolution, Orbiter photographed the entire moon in a series of different orbits ranging in altitude from about 30 to 3,750 miles. Lunar Orbiter was one of the most successful of all U.S. space programs; in 1966-67 it scored five successes in as many launches, returning about 1,000 large-area frames and making possible production of lunar maps 100 times more detailed than those based on earth observations.

From the vast Surveyor/Lunar Orbiter storehouse of photographic knowledge, NASA proceeded to select the Apollo landing sites, matching areas of most scientific interest with the safety considerations of Lunar Module descent, approach, and touchdown.

By early 1969, the selection group had settled upon the targets for the first 10 lunar landing missions. Picked for the first manned landing was the

Sea of Tranquillity in the eastern part of the visible face of the moon. For the second visit, NASA decided upon another sea—or *mare*—in the western region. Filling in an area that covers most of the moonface width and ranges well above and below the lunar equator, other sites selected take in the valleys, the highlands, the craters, certain areas characterized by possible volcanic material, and a zone that adjoins a great trench-like "rill." In combination, the 10 sites offer the broadest possible scientific coverage, because each zone differs from the others in physical features.

If further landings are authorized, NASA contemplates exploration closer to the lunar poles, possibly even on the "back side" of the moon, the side never seen from earth. The comprehensive photo-library built up by the unmanned pathfinders can meet the basic mission planning requirements, but if additional information of a specific nature is needed, NASA has available the most versatile spacecraft of them all—Apollo itself.

Rehearsals for the Moon 8

CHAPTER

THE TWO LUNAR-ORBIT DRESS REHEARSALS for the moon landing —Apollo 8 and Apollo 10—certainly rank among the most daring ventures in the history of exploration. They were awesome demonstrations of American technological competence and accomplishments of the first magnitude for United States prestige. And they brought the space program new support from the American people, suddenly awakened to the fact that man could—and soon would—make reality of the age-old dream of landing on the moon.

For all that, Apollo 8 and Apollo 10 were not even "missions," strictly speaking. A mission, in technical parlance, is an operational flight of a proven vehicle. The only actual missions in the Apollo program are those in which man sets foot on the moon. All the preliminaries were simply "tests." It is a hair-splitting distinction, but one which underscores the extraordinary demands of Apollo testing; even flights into lunar orbit are simply preparatory steps toward the real goal.

Never in the annals of aerospace development has there been a test program even remotely approaching that of Apollo. NASA contractors were forced to build elaborate test facilities, to devise automated test equipment which, in some cases, was more complex than the flightware it was testing, and to spend more time checking out the equipment than it took to build it.

Proving flights represented only a small percentage of the hundreds of millions of man-hours expended in the testing phase. The size, complexity, and cost of the flying segments made impossible the type of test program employed in airplane or guided missile development, wherein the vehicle is flown a hundred or more times before being assigned to operational

In the last major rehearsal step before the first lunar landing, the Apollo 10 Command Module dropped into the sea after a moon-orbiting trip lasting eight days and carrying astronauts within ten miles of the moon's surface.

service, becoming progressively more reliable through test, failure, repair, and retest. A Saturn V/Apollo launch costs upwards of $300,000,000, so it cannot be used to isolate "bugs" for later correction; its purpose is to verify equipment made as nearly perfect as possible by endless, repetitive ground tests.

Every item destined for later incorporation in a Saturn V/Apollo stack, from a tiny sensor to the complete spacecraft, is subjected to continual rigorous inspection and test, examined by both humans and the near-infallible automatic test equipment. A part is tested individually, then as an assembly of several parts. A number of assemblies are checked out as subsystems, the subsystems merged into systems and tested again. Every system is examined separately in a laboratory or in a specially built facility where most of the conditions of space flight can be simulated. Then it is checked out in its actual position in the space vehicle, where its interaction with other systems can be observed. Finally, complete modules or stages are tested as integrated units. This lengthy but necessary procedure involves literally millions of test operations.

But no matter how carefully a system is ground-tested, no matter how efficient the human examiners and the robot checkout equipment, no component of Saturn V/Apollo can be considered ready for a lunar mission until it has demonstrated its capability in space. For this purpose, NASA set up a schedule of a score of flights, most of them unmanned, and, mindful of costs, the space agency used the Saturn V only where its great payload-boosting capability was necessary; three smaller launch vehicles were assigned the boost functions for the less demanding, earlier phases of the program.

Flight Tests without Saturn V

To the casual observer, the Apollo flight test program may have seemed a haphazard operation, involving as it did the different boosters, different payloads, flight paths ranging from suborbital to around the moon, and maneuvers which appear to the layman to have little to do with the end goal of preparing the space vehicle for lunar landing missions. It was, however, anything but haphazard. Every test operation fitted neatly into a grand mosaic. The program started with simple, unmanned near-earth tests of individual components, then built up in carefully considered sequence to manned lunar-orbit dress rehearsals.

The first item of the stack to undergo test in flight was the launch escape system. For this series, NASA developed a special launch vehicle called

Little Joe II. A simple, relatively inexpensive, solid-propellant rocket, Little Joe II was capable of boosting a test article at velocities comparable to those of Saturn V in the early phase of a launch; it was not intended to send a payload into orbit, only to check out the escape rocket at altitudes up to about 40 miles. The payloads were replicas of the Apollo Command and Service Modules called *boilerplates,* research vehicles which simulated the size, shape, structure, mass, and center of gravity of the spacecraft modules but which contained none of Apollo's complex systems. Instrumented to send back engineering data, their purpose was to verify the basic spacecraft design under flight conditions.

The *abort flights,* as the space agency termed the escape rocket tests, began late in 1963 at White Sands Test Range in New Mexico. The first was a zero-speed abort, in other words, a simulation of an emergency on the pad before liftoff; the launch escape system yanked the boilerplate Command Module free of the stack and propelled it to high altitude, where

LITTLE JOE II

A single-stage launch
  vehicle used for testing
  the launch escape system
  during emergency abort
  at various altitudes
HEIGHT—33 feet
DIAMETER—13 feet plus
  fins
WEIGHT LOADED—
  170,000 pounds
PROPULSION—various
  combinations of Algol
  and Recruit solid-rocket
  motors, depending on
  test requirements
MAXIMUM THRUST—
  850,000 pounds
PAYLOAD—20,000 pounds
  to 900,000 feet altitude
  80,000 pounds to lower
  altitudes
FIRST USE—11/7/63 in
  Apollo pad abort test

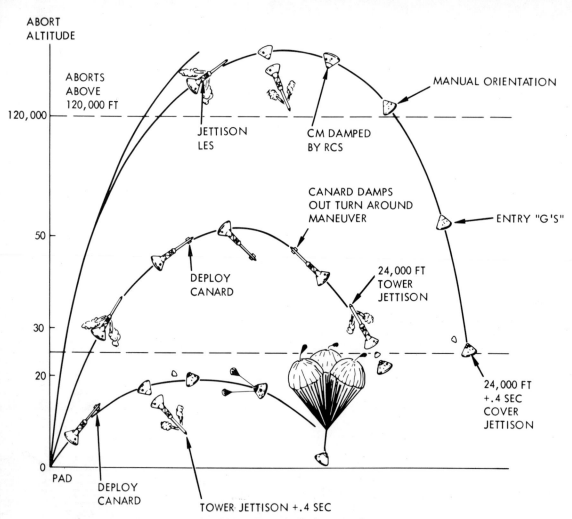

ABORT
ALTITUDE

ABORTS
ABOVE
120,000 FT

120,000

MANUAL ORIENTATION

JETTISON
LES

CM DAMPED
BY RCS

CANARD DAMPS
OUT TURN AROUND
MANEUVER

50

ENTRY "G'S"

DEPLOY
CANARD

24,000 FT
TOWER
JETTISON

30

20

24,000 FT
+.4 SEC
COVER
JETTISON

0

PAD

DEPLOY
CANARD

TOWER JETTISON +.4 SEC

Starting in late 1963, the first boilerplate Apollo spacecraft
were used to test the three ways in which the launch escape
system operates (depending on altitude of the abort). It was
declared qualified little more than two years later.

the parachute landing system deployed automatically and lowered the
capsule to earth. Over the next two years, NASA conducted five more tests,
simulating aborts at higher speeds and greater altitudes. All were successful, and the launch escape tower was pronounced ready for manned flight.

Running concurrently with the abort flights was a second series of
boilerplate tests launched by *Saturn I*, the baby of the Saturn family, yet
by far the largest launch vehicle developed by the United States up to that
time. In this series, test conductors were interested in the launch-to-exit
phase, or how the basic design of the Command and Service Modules
reacted to the stresses of atmospheric and near-space flight from liftoff to
orbit. The boilerplates were not heat-shielded and were permitted to burn

SATURN IB

Launch vehicle for testing the Apollo spacecraft in earth orbit

HEIGHT—224 feet
DIAMETER—21 feet
WEIGHT (dry)—152,000 pounds
WEIGHT (loaded)—1,300,000 pounds
S-IB FIRST STAGE PROPULSION—8 H-1 engines of
   200,000 pounds thrust each
S-IB BURN TIME—2.5 minutes
S-IB PROPELLANTS: fuel—kerosene (42,000 gallons)
   oxidizer—liquid oxygen (67,000 gallons)
S-IVB SECOND STAGE—same as third stage on Saturn V
   (see page 28)
FIRST FLIGHT—2/26/66

While major flight tests went on, less conspicuous tests of all kinds were being carried out. In an anechoic chamber *(above),* which simulates space in terms of radio waves, communications and other electronic equipment is checked for interference. Spacesuit tests *(left)* involved measuring oxygen use and metabolic rate during strenuous activity, such as would be needed in moon-walking.

up in re-entry. Again, all five flights were successful, and the basic design was verified for unmanned space operations.

On February 26, 1966, NASA launched from Cape Kennedy what shall here be termed *Apollo 1*, although at that time the space agency employed more complicated designations. Apollo 1 marked the first flight of a "live" basic spacecraft with many of its systems operating. For tests of the thrusters in both the Command and Service Modules, and for firing the big Service Module engine, the spacecraft had to carry a nearly full load of propellants. The added weight necessitated use of *Saturn IB*, a launch vehicle larger and considerably more powerful than its predecessor. Saturn IB, sometimes called the *Uprated Saturn*, is a two-stage booster whose upper stage is the same S-IVB that serves as top stage in the Saturn V vehicle, so the flight served to check out one segment of the moonbooster as well as the spacecraft.

Apollo 1 was a suborbital flight that followed a huge parabola from Cape Kennedy to a point 5,000 miles downrange in the Atlantic Ocean. Primary objectives were to confirm the "structural integrity" of the space-craft, to check out a number of the major internal systems, to fire the Apollo Service engine for the first time, and to make the initial test of the heat shield.

S-IVB injected the spacecraft into the proper trajectory at an altitude of about 100 miles, separated, and fell back to earth while Apollo continued to climb in coasting flight. At the peak of the parabola, the spacecraft's altitude was thruster-adjusted so that the conical nose was pointing earthward at a steep angle. Then the engine fired, accelerating Apollo to the proper velocity for the heat shield test, and the Service Module separated from the Command Module. Simulating a descent from earth orbit, the Command Module thrusters turned the spacecraft around blunt-bottom-first and the capsule plunged into the atmosphere at close to 17,500 miles per hour. This provided the first of three checkpoints of the heat shield's perform-ance "envelope."

Apollo 2, launched July 5, 1966, carried no spacecraft. Its primary pur-pose was to check out the S-IVB stage under conditions approximating those of a lunar mission. This involved sending S-IVB into orbit for a revolution and a half, maneuvering it by firing its auxiliary propulsion system, and steering it toward a translunar injection. Of particular interest was the behavior of the tricky liquid hydrogen fuel in weightless state, but it posed no special problems.

The *Apollo 3* flight, made August 25, 1966, was essentially a repeat of Apollo 1 as regards checking out the engine, thrusters, and internal systems, but it was different from the standpoint of the heat shield test. This time, Saturn IB gave the spacecraft a little extra push, not enough to inject it into orbit, but to direct it into a flat suborbital path covering three-quarters of the way around the earth. Instead of the steep descent angle of Apollo 1, the Command Module re-entered over the Pacific in a long, shallow trajectory, absorbing greater heat because of a longer period of exposure to atmospheric friction. The heat shield met the challenge, the second of its three planned trials. Upon successful conclusion of Apollo 3,

A fire in an Apollo spacecraft atop a stationary Saturn launch vehicle at Cape Kennedy killed astronauts Grissom, White, and Chaffee on January 27, 1967. The Apollo program was held up while the spacecraft was redesigned to incorporate more safety features.

the basic spacecraft was qualified for manned earth-orbital flight.

The next step was to have been a complete earth-orbital checkout of the basic spacecraft by a human crew; the flight was scheduled for February, 1967. But on January 27, 1967, the Apollo program suffered a staggering setback. A flash fire in the Command Module during a routine prelaunch test cost the lives of astronauts Virgil I. Grissom, Edward H. White II, and Roger B. Chaffee. Spacecraft modifications dictated by the ensuing investigation caused a long hiatus in the flight program, and in an effort to regain lost ground, NASA revised its test plan. Instead of the relatively simple agenda of manned systems checkout in earth orbit, the space agency boldly decided to go all-out on Apollo 4, combining several major objectives into the first unmanned launch of Saturn V.

The Saturn V Debut on Apollo 4

On November 9, 1967, NASA launched *Apollo 4,* the "Big Shot," as it was being called. Big it was, in every sense of the word: in hardware dimensions, in scope, in its importance to future programming. Despite the fact that it carried no human payload, Apollo 4 was at that time the most significant step in American space research history. The flight represented not only the initial rehearsal for the lunar landing missions, it was also a bid for renewed public confidence, dealt a shattering blow by the tragic accident.

The Apollo 4 stack included all segments except the Lunar Module, not yet ready for test; in its place was a dummy of the same weight as the real thing, covered by a genuine adapter, or shroud. There were heavy odds against complete success of Apollo 4 because of the complicated maneuvers planned and the uncertainties of first-time operation of so much of the stack. For example, neither the S-IC basic stage nor the S-II second stage had ever been subjected to flight. The big F-1 engine had never flown; the second stage J-2 powerplant had, but singly, never as a cluster of five. Predecessor versions of the Instrument Unit had operated aboard Saturn I and Saturn IB, but the Saturn V brain, considerably different, was new to space. So were the Lunar Module adapter and the launch escape tower. Of all the great stack, only the basic spacecraft and the S-IVB stage could boast time in space.

Apollo 4 ignored the odds and began to demonstrate its capability from the moment of liftoff. Both the lower stages performed perfectly, the launch escape tower was jettisoned at exactly the planned instant, and the Instrument Unit directed the spacecraft—with S-IVB still attached—into the precise orbit programmed.

APOLLO TEST PROGRAM CHRONOLOGY

up to the first flight of Saturn V

DATE	LAUNCH VEHICLE	SPACECRAFT	EVENT AND RESULTS
7/29/60			Project Apollo—a program to land men on the moon—was announced by NASA
5/25/61			President John F. Kennedy proposed a national goal of landing a man on the moon before the end of the decade
4/11/61			NASA awarded the first contract for production of part (the second stage) of an advanced Saturn rocket
11/28/61			NASA announced the awarding of the first contract for development of the Apollo spacecraft (what eventually became the Command and Service Modules)
1/25/62			Marshall Space Flight Center was given the assignment of developing the 3-stage Saturn V
7/11/62			NASA announced that lunar orbit rendezvous was the method selected for a lunar landing, necessitating development of a Lunar Module; plans to develop Saturn IB were announced
11/7/62			NASA awarded a contract for development of the Lunar Module
11/7/63	Little Joe II	Boilerplate Apollo	First flight test; test of launch escape system during pad abort; successful
1/29/64	Saturn I		First orbital flight of Saturn I; lifted 37,900 pounds into orbit
5/13/64	Little Joe II	Boilerplate Apollo	High-speed abort test with high stress; successful, though one of the three parachutes cut loose
5/28/64	Saturn I	Boilerplate Apollo	First orbital flight of Command Module; proved compatibility of spacecraft and launch vehicle
9/18/64	Saturn I	Boilerplate Apollo	Orbital test of Saturn I; declared operational
12/8/64	Little Joe II	Boilerplate Apollo	Test of high-speed abort and earth landing system; successful
2/16/65	Saturn I	Boilerplate Command and modified Service Module	First operational flight of Saturn I; launched first Pegasus meteoroid detection satellite using Service Module shell for protection; successful
5/19/65	Little Joe II	Boilerplate Apollo	High-altitude launch escape system test; guidance malfunction caused premature abort at low altitude, but system worked perfectly
5/25/65	Saturn I	Boilerplate Apollo	Second launch of a Pegasus satellite; successful
6/29/65	Little Joe II	Boilerplate Command Module	Pad abort, testing all systems of the launch escape system; successful
7/30/65	Saturn I	Boilerplate Apollo and Lunar Module adapter	Launch of Pegasus satellite within Lunar Module adapter housing; panels opened properly and satellite was released in orbit; last flight of Saturn I
10/20/65			First actual Apollo spacecraft was completed and accepted by NASA
1/20/66	Little Joe II	Flight-rated Command Module	Final tumbling abort test, using actual spacecraft; successful; launch escape system was declared qualified
2/26/66	Saturn IB	Flight-rated Apollo	First unmanned flight of the Command and Service Modules; first flight of Saturn IB; test of thrusters and Service Propulsion restart; successful, though Service Propulsion engine did not produce full thrust
7/5/66	Saturn IB		First orbital flight of Saturn IB; test of liquid hydrogen behavior and S-IVB restart capability; successful
8/25/66	Saturn IB	Flight-rated Apollo	Unmanned suborbital flight to test heat shield; successful
1/27/67			A flash fire in a Command Module atop a Saturn IB caused the deaths of three astronauts
4/9/67			The board reviewing the Apollo fire presented its findings and recommended a number of changes in the spacecraft

Some 3 hours after injection into orbit, the J-2 engine of the S-IVB stage thundered into action, its first restart. It burned for more than 5 minutes while the Instrument Unit guided the stack into a simulated lunar trajectory designed to loft the spacecraft to an altitude of more than 11,000 miles. Then S-IVB and the Instrument Unit separated and Apollo was on its own in its first deep-space venture.

After a brief checkout burn of the Apollo engine, the spacecraft was nudged into the proper attitude for another important test called the *cold soak*. The Command Module was positioned so that half of the conical capsule was oriented toward the harsh, undiluted sunlight of space and the other half was in cold shadow. This was a test of the efficiency of the spacecraft's outer walls at simultaneous extremes of temperature, and it also afforded an opportunity to observe the environmental control system's ability to maintain proper temperatures inside the Command Module while the capsule was both very hot and very cold outside. Apollo maintained the cold-soak attitude for 4½ hours, a thorough exposure to deep-space conditions and a first for a spacecraft designed to carry men.

Throughout the "soaking" period, Apollo was in coasting flight, moving farther from earth toward the apogee, or high point, of its elliptical orbit. During this time, there were continuous automatic checkouts of each of the spacecraft's major systems, operating for the first time in the deep-space environment.

The last major test of Apollo 4 was another study of heat shield performance, but this time at the speed of 24,400 miles per hour, the velocity of return from a lunar mission. Having passed apogee and started "downhill" toward earth, Apollo was gaining speed rapidly. Not enough, however, to satisfy the heat shield qualification requirement, so speed had to be increased by a second burn of the spacecraft engine. Although the engine was designed for as many as 36 firings on a single mission, it had not, until Apollo 4, made more than one. But the second burn was as successful as everything else on the flight, and the desired velocity was attained.

Having separated from the Service Module, the Command Module plummeted into the atmosphere, recording a maximum temperature on its outer surface of 5,050 degrees Fahrenheit, about twice the greatest heat load experienced by Mercury or Gemini spacecraft on re-entry. The heat shield proved up to its assignment, and interior temperatures remained well within human-tolerable limits.

Some 500 miles north of Hawaii, Apollo 4 splashed down only a few miles from the waiting aircraft carrier USS *Bennington*, a perfect end to a perfect mission. In addition to the primary objectives, thousands of minor

In the momentous maiden launch of the mighty Saturn V on
November 9, 1967, the giant rocket sent an Apollo spacecraft
11,000 miles out in space. All systems worked superbly in
the "Big Shot" and manned flights were scheduled.

tests and engineering measurements had been accomplished in only 8 hours
and 37 minutes. The Big Shot had turned out to be just that, a giant step
that put the once-derailed Apollo program back on the track.

The Final Unmanned Tests

At the conclusion of Apollo 4, all of the major segments of the stack had
had at least one big test in space, with the exception of the Lunar Module.
Two and a half months later, on January 22, 1968, the moonbug made its
flight debut, unmanned and alone, without its companion Command and
Service Modules. The relatively light weight of the single module—just over
15 tons—permitted NASA to use the smaller Saturn IB launch vehicle.

On *Apollo 5,* the S-IVB stage inserted the Lunar Module into a low-
altitude orbit and the two units separated successfully. After a 4-hour
period of coasting flight, the flight plan called for two burns each of the
descent and ascent engines. The first burn of the descent engine was to
have run for almost 7 minutes, but the Lunar Module's computer "goofed"
and shut down the engine after only 4.3 seconds.

This minor malfunction caused controllers on the ground to change the
flight plan and scrub a planned 12-minute burn which would have simu-

lated a descent to the moon. Instead, two very brief burns—26 seconds each—were substituted.

Apollo 5 ran through the remaining test sequence without a hitch. The ascent and descent stages were separated, permitting the ascent portion of the moon taxi to simulate a climb from the lunar surface. Its engine fired once for a minute, then a second time for 6 minutes. All of the internal systems performed well.

In the post-flight analysis, NASA officials decided that Apollo 5 could be termed a success despite the one malfunction. The descent engine had operated for less than a minute, compared with the 19 minutes planned. It had, however, made three good, though brief, burns. It was determined that the Lunar Module could be considered qualified for manned flight, but that the earth-orbital tests would have to be repeated under human control.

With Apollo equipment production and ground checkout now in high gear, NASA was able to mount another test only 10 weeks after Apollo 5. This flight—*Apollo 6*—was essentially a re-run of Apollo 4 to get a "second opinion" on the performance of the equipment which had operated flawlessly on the Big Shot.

Apollo 4 was a tough act to follow but Apollo 6 nearly duplicated it. Through 95 percent of the flight everything was "nominal," just as planned —the launch to parking orbit; the restart of the J-2 engine to initiate deep-space trajectory; the burn of the Apollo engine; a 6-hour cold soak; the first in-space test of the new Command Module outward-opening hatch, the major modification dictated by the investigation of the fire; and the climb to a new high apogee of 13,840 miles.

Not until the "downhill" phase, where the spacecraft headed back toward earth, did a problem arise. Apollo 6 was supposed to re-enter at the same speed as Apollo 4—24,400 miles per hour. But the Apollo engine had burned overlong on the way up to apogee and it had insufficient fuel left to accelerate the spacecraft to the desired velocity. Apollo 6 re-entered at less than 22,000 miles per hour. After post-flight examination of the minimal heat-erosion of the outer surface, it was concluded that the heat shield would have had no trouble countering the higher re-entry speed planned; since the shield had earlier demonstrated its effectiveness anyway, it was qualified for lunar flight.

The First Manned Apollo Flight

At this point, everything in the stack except the "rookie" Lunar Module had made at least two successful space flights. It was time for a human crew to take over the Apollo controls. NASA scheduled *Apollo 7* for October 11, 1968, and assigned Walter M. Schirra, Jr., Donn F. Eisele, and Walter Cunningham as the first Apollo crew. The launch vehicle was a Saturn IB, because once again there was no Lunar Module aboard; there were no production models available, nor would there be until 1969..

Aside from the fact that it was manned, there was little dramatic about Apollo 7. It was a routine earth-orbital test of all systems under the conditions for which the spacecraft was designed: control by man instead of a robot programmer. The major new element of the test program was duration. None of the unmanned flights had lasted longer than a day, but a lunar mission takes a week or more, so the systems had to demonstrate their prowess in repetitive, long-time operations. All of the complex equipment operated as it was supposed to for almost 11 full days, leading a NASA official to comment that the flight was "101 percent successful" because the systems had been asked to perform extra tests conceived after the flight was spaceborne.

Apollo 7 splashed down within sight of the recovery carrier USS *Essex*. If there was one tiny flaw in the entire operation, it was the fact that the Command Module landed in the water upside down. This was not hazardous, since the possibility of nose-down splash had been taken into consideration in designing the capsule and the module is both stable and floatable upside down. It was, however, uncomfortable, since the craft bobs and spins more with its conical nose in the water, and Schirra became seasick.

Apollo 8 to the Moon

With Apollo 7, NASA had scored three successes in 1968. The fourth, the *pièce de résistance* of a year of incredible progress, was launched December 21 with Frank Borman, James A. Lovell, and William A. Anders in the Command Module couches. The most dramatic space flight ever made until that time, *Apollo 8* astounded the world as the trio directed a Command/Service Module spacecraft into orbit around the moon, made 10 revolutions, then returned safely to earth to splash down in the Pacific just 147 hours after launch. The flight, which covered 570,000 miles, was particularly notable because it marked the first time man had operated in a gravity field other than earth's. From the viewpoint of the test engineer, however, there were a number of less publicized events of Apollo 8 that were of equal or even greater importance to the success of the lunar landing program.

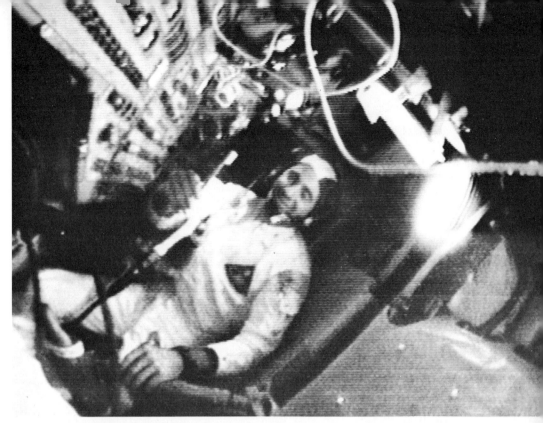

Millions of television viewers back on earth joined the
Apollo 8 astronauts in space during six live telecasts. Anders
demonstrated the difficulties of weightlessness, but the
great thrill was the sight of earth as seen from space.

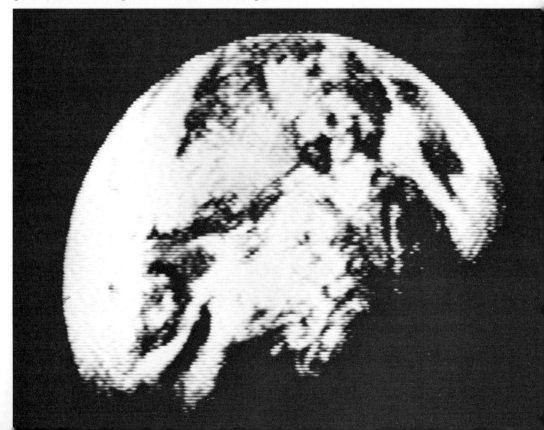

"Not a very inviting place to live or work," concluded the
Apollo 8 astronauts as they became the first men to near the
moon. Studies of their orbits revealed mass concentrations of dense matter beneath the surface which create
unexpected variations in the gravitational field.

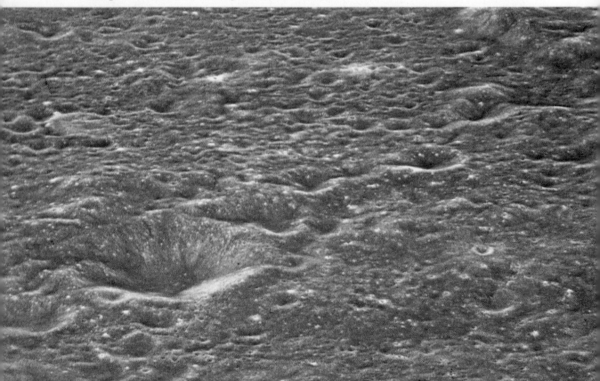

It was the maiden launch of a manned Saturn V, so all of the operations from launch to translunar injection were being performed for the first time under human direction. The optical star-sighting system got its first checkout; no one had ever navigated in deep space before, but the precision with which the crew handled the task left little doubt that Apollo 8 could have flown to the moon and back without assistance from the ground. The tracking and communications stations gained valuable experience. Long distance voice and TV transmissions involved another "first"—the initial workout for the spacecraft's four-leaf-clover deep-space high-gain antenna which receives and transmits with great signal strength.

A test of particular interest to NASA planners was the rotation of the spacecraft throughout the flight in what astronauts call the "barbecue mode." This amounts to a reversal of the tests involved in the "cold soak" operations of Apollo 4 and 6. On those flights, NASA employed the cold soak to subject internal systems to the greatest temperature extremes they would ever experience. For manned flights, NASA seeks to minimize, rather than maximize, temperature effect. This is accomplished, as it was on Apollo 8, by rolling the spacecraft slowly; a brief firing of the thrusters starts a rotation around the spacecraft's fore-and-aft axis, like a barbecue on a spit, at the rate of one revolution per hour. In this mode, the heat of bright sunlight and the cold of shadowed space are distributed equally over the outer surface, easing the load on the environmental control system. The rotation continues until corrected and does not bother the astronauts; the movement, after all, is at the same rate as the barely discernible motion of the minute hand on a clock.

The most important accomplishments of Apollo 8, from the standpoint of the test program, were the *supercritical* maneuvers. On a lunar landing mission, there are seven steps which present the most operational difficulties and the greatest hazard. They include the insertion into lunar orbit, requiring a precise subtraction of velocity; the separation in lunar orbit of the Lunar Module from the basic spacecraft and the start of the descent; the approach and touchdown on the moon's surface; the blastoff from the moon with the ascent engine; the rendezvous and docking with the basic spacecraft after ascent to lunar orbit; the *must* firing of the Apollo main engine to take the astronauts out of lunar orbit; and the always-risky fireballing re-entry, which allows a margin of aiming error of only one degree. Apollo 8 executed three of these supercritical maneuvers for the first time: lunar orbit entry and exit, and earth-re-entry at lunar return speed, which reached 24,687 miles per hour, at that time the fastest a human had ever flown.

Apollo 9 and the Lunar Module

The next step, *Apollo 9*, was an extensive performance check of the Lunar Module, never before flown under manned control. Launched February 28, 1969, Apollo 9 was crewed by James A. McDivitt, David R. Scott, and Russell Schweickart, who put both the Lunar Module and the basic spacecraft through a series of first-time maneuvers in the course of a 10-day flight in earth orbit.

The first test, which came 2 hours and 50 minutes after launch, was the *transposition and docking*, also known as the "turnaround" maneuver. This maneuver is necessitated by the fact that, in launch configuration, there is no way for the astronauts to transfer from the basic spacecraft to the Lunar Module; the Service Module is interposed between. This odd arrangement is dictated by safety considerations; the Command Module must be topmost in the stack so it can be pulled free by the escape tower in an emergency. It is an excellent configuration for launch, but it is unsatisfactory in space, so the modules must be realigned.

On Apollo 9, the astronauts first actuated a mechanism which popped open the clamshell panels of the adapter shrouding the Lunar Module. Then, using the Service Module's thrusters, McDivitt flew the basic spacecraft about 50 feet away from what amounted to a second spacecraft: the Lunar Module still connected to the S-IVB upper stage of the launch vehicle. McDivitt then turned the basic spacecraft around so that it was "nose to nose" with the Lunar Module. He closed the distance and jockeyed his spacecraft until the probe in the Command Module slipped into the drogue in the Lunar Module. The fittings locked automatically so that the hatches of each module formed a tunnel connecting the two spacecraft. McDivitt again used his thrusters to back off, pulling the Lunar Module free from the S-IVB. The rearranged spacecraft was then in *lunar configuration*.

The next three days of Apollo 9 were devoted to a lengthy series of systems checkouts and performance studies of the complete spacecraft, flying for the first time as a three-module unit. Among major tests during this period were multiple burns of the Apollo primary engine and the Lunar Module's thrusters, fired while the spacecraft remained docked together, and the first crew transfer, in which McDivitt and Schweickart entered the Lunar Module, "powered it up," and ran through a check of its systems.

Highlight of the fourth day was the first extravehicular activity of the Apollo program; Schweickart stepped out onto the "porch" of the Lunar Module, a small platform adjacent to the hatch used for egress to the moon, and photographed the earth and both spacecraft.

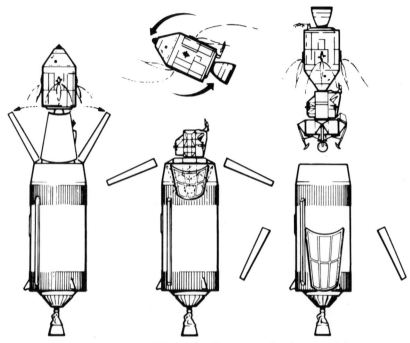

The flight of Apollo 9 in earth orbit tested the transposition and docking maneuver. Docking occurs twice during a lunar mission—once on the way to the moon and again when the Lunar Module rises from the lunar surface to rejoin the Command Module. During the transposition the last segment of the Saturn V is discarded in space.

A big test of Apollo 9 came on the fifth day when McDivitt and Schweickart again entered the Lunar Module, powered up its systems and this time separated from the basic spacecraft. Firing the Lunar Module descent engine, they sent their moonbug into a separate orbit. With two additional burns of the engine they made orbital changes corresponding to the type of maneuvers that precede an actual lunar landing, then the descent stage was jettisoned. Using the smaller ascent-stage engine, the Lunar Module crew directed their craft into a new orbit that permitted it to "catch up" with the basic spacecraft. The ensuing rendezvous and docking, which saw the first use of the vital rendezvous radar, went flawlessly and the equipment was qualified for use at lunar distance.

After McDivitt and Schweickart returned to the Command Module, the Lunar Module was separated, eventually to burn up on atmospheric re-entry. Apollo 9 remained aloft an additional five days while the astronauts conducted further checkouts of the basic spacecraft, then made a near-perfect landing in the Atlantic Ocean.

During the 5½ hours it was separated from the basic spacecraft, the Lunar Module had demonstrated a remarkable degree of systems reliability. But its operations had been confined to earth orbit. Before NASA could signal "go" for the lunar landing, the taxicraft had to perform similar maneuvers in the environment for which it was designed—the one-sixth gravity of the moon.

High over the Mississippi Valley, the Apollo 9 crew put Gumdrop (the Command Module) and Spider (the Lunar Module) through their paces. Stepping out on the porch of Spider, LM Pilot Schweickart photographed Gumdrop Pilot Scott at the open hatch. The space walk tested alternatives to going through the tunnel between the joined craft.

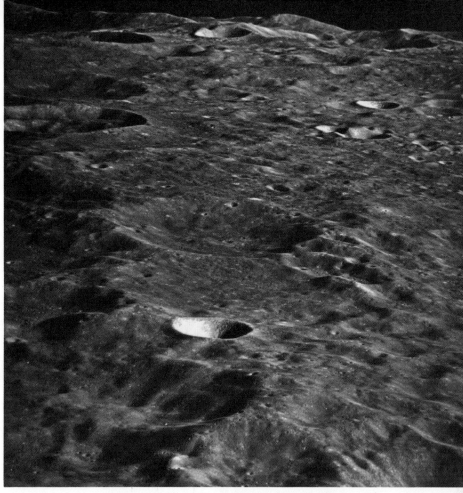

Apollo 10, the final step before the lunar landing, took the Lunar Module to less than 10 miles above the moon's surface. On a real landing mission it would, at that point, have ignited its engine for a controlled descent to put American man on the moon.

Apollo 10, The Final Dress Rehearsal

Launched May 18, 1969, *Apollo 10* was manned by Thomas P. Stafford, Eugene A. Cernan, and John W. Young. In trajectory, Apollo 10 was generally similar to Apollo 8; it made a round trip to the moon covering 577,000 miles in 8 days and 39 seconds. Apollo 10 spent a longer time in lunar orbit —31 revolutions—and it experienced an even faster re-entry—24,790 miles per hour.

The big difference was the inclusion in the stack of the Lunar Module and its descent to within 9.4 miles of the lunar surface. Some 98 hours after launch, with the spacecraft orbiting 69 miles above the moon, Stafford and Cernan entered the Lunar Module, activated its systems, and separated

APOLLO TEST PROGRAM CHRONOLOGY

Apollo 4—Apollo 10

Flight	Date	Crew	Launch vehicle	Tests and events
Apollo 4	11/9/67		Saturn V	First Saturn V launch; spacecraft entered atmosphere at 24,913 mph in first heat-shield test at lunar return speed; temperatures reached about 5,000°F; successful for both launch vehicle and spacecraft
Apollo 5	1/22/68		Saturn IB	First space flight of the Lunar Module; tested ascent and descent engines and ability to abort lunar landing and return to orbit; successful
Apollo 6	4/4/68		Saturn V	Second flight of Saturn V; partial success; second stage engines cut off prematurely; third stage failed to restart, but Service Propulsion System burned for a record time; spacecraft was declared qualified for manned flight
Apollo 7	10/11- 11/22/68	Schirra Eisele Cunningham	Saturn IB	First manned flight of Command and Service Modules; Lunar Module was a dummy; 3-man crew was in orbit for 260 hours, simulated Lunar Module docking by approaching to within 4 feet of S-IVB stage; other tests included station-keeping with the S-IVB, short and long Service Propulsion burns, first live telecasts to earth, use of tracking and communications networks; successful
Apollo 8	12/21- 12/27/68	Borman Lovell Anders	Saturn V	First manned flight to the moon; Command and Service Modules and the crew made 10 lunar orbits at altitude of 69 miles; Service Propulsion System successfully performed critical burns for lunar orbit insertion and transearth injection; live telecasts of deep-space views of earth and close-ups of the lunar surface; first manned launch of Saturn V; successful
Apollo 9	3/3- 3/13/69	McDivitt Scott Schweickart	Saturn V	First test of Command and Service Modules working with Lunar Module in space; in 151 earth orbits, crew performed transposition and docking and separation and rendezvous; McDivitt and Schweickart transferred to Lunar Module 3 times, flew it in separate orbit for 6½ hours; Schweickart performed 37-minute space walk; successful
Apollo 10	5/18- 5/26/69	Stafford Cernan Young	Saturn V	First test of Lunar Module in lunar environment; crew made 31 lunar orbits at 69-mile altitude; 2 men in Lunar Module flew within 50,000 feet of the moon, simulating landing and ascent, then rendezvoused with the Command Module; successful; all modules were declared qualified for the first actual lunar landing

from the basic spacecraft. During the next 8½ hours, Stafford and Cernan flew the Lunar Module through a sequence of maneuvers designed to duplicate as closely as possible those of a lunar landing mission—except for the final approach and touchdown.

Firing the descent engine to reduce velocity, they dropped into a low-altitude orbit, sweeping twice over Apollo Landing Site Number Two in the moon's Sea of Tranquillity. After photographing the lunar surface from man's closest vantage point up to that time, they jettisoned the descent stage and used the ascent engine to enter a new orbital path that took them back to the waiting basic spacecraft piloted by Young. The rendezvous and docking went smoothly and, with all three astronauts reunited in the Command Module, the ascent stage was separated. Blasted out of lunar orbit by the main engine, Apollo 10 made a 54-hour return to earth and splashed down in the Pacific within sight of the recovery carrier USS *Princeton*.

Apollo 10 provided the best-yet color photographs of the moon, essential to planning for manned landings, a further check of the reliability of the Lunar Module's rendezvous radar, and a partial test of the landing radar. Most importantly, it accomplished two more of the supercritical maneuvers: descent from lunar orbit and return to the basic spacecraft. There remained untried only two of the seven big steps, the most critical of the supercriticals—the lunar touchdown and the subsequent blastoff. Apollo 10 raised NASA's "confidence factor" to an unprecedented level and prompted the agency's decision, made early in June, 1969, to go for the moon on Apollo 11.

Eagle on the Moon

CHAPTER 9

JULY 16, 1969. MOON-LAUNCH DAY at Cape Kennedy. Along the shores of the Atlantic, and the banks of the Indian and Banana rivers, a million spectators sought vantage points for the blast-off. Around the world, hundreds of millions watched the launch preliminaries on home and public television screens.

T minus 10. The last technician had withdrawn from Pad 39A. The Saturn V/Apollo bird stood tall and majestic on its launcher, patiently submitting to one last electronic scrutiny of its complex innards. Far above the launcher's base, scanning the cockpit displays, were three astronauts bound on man's greatest adventure.

In the left-side couch was Neil Armstrong, commander of Apollo 11. In the center, Edwin Aldrin, Lunar Module pilot. On the right, Michael Collins, Command Module pilot and the "lonely man" of Apollo 11; he was fated to remain in lunar orbit while Armstrong and Aldrin descended to the surface to become the first men on the moon.

Three miles from the pad, in the launch control center, a hundred men stared intently at their consoles. All the panel lights were green-for-go. The countdown clock on the wall raced toward zero, ticking off the remaining time to liftoff in tenths of a second. Then suddenly, "Ignition!"

With a Vesuvian roar, the five mighty engines of the first stage sprang to life. Sheets of fire darted along the flame trench, obscured by billowing clouds of steam as the exhaust deflector was deluged with water. For a nine-second eternity the great stack was immobile while the computer in the base of the launcher verified that full thrust—7,600,000 pounds—had been attained. Then, slowly at first, the 6,485,000-pound space vehicle lifted off the pad, barely clearing the launch tower in the first 10 seconds.

The Apollo 11 mission, placing two men on the moon, included 15 key steps: 1) liftoff from Cape Kennedy; 2) checkout in earth orbit; 3) the S-IVB burn for translunar injection; 4) turnaround and docking; 5) mid-course correction; 6) retrofiring of the SPS engine for lunar orbit; 7) lunar orbit; 8) separation of the Lunar Module; 9) landing on the moon; 10) rendezvous and docking of ascent stage and Command Module; 11) jettisoning the Lunar Module; 12) transearth injection; 13) mid-course correction; 14) jettisoning the Service Module; and 15) re-entry.

TARGET: THE MOON

DIAMETER—2,160 miles
CIRCUMFERENCE—6,790 miles
DISTANCE FROM EARTH—238,857 miles (mean); (221,463 miles at minimum—perigee—to 252,710 miles at maximum—apogee)
LUNAR DAY AND NIGHT—14 earth-days each
MEAN ORBITAL VELOCITY—2,287 miles per hour

PERIOD OF ROTATION AROUND EARTH— 27 days, 7 hours, 43 minutes
SURFACE TEMPERATURE plus 250°F (sun at zenith); minus 280°F (at night)
SURFACE GRAVITY—1/6 that of earth
MASS—1/100 that of earth
VOLUME—1/50 that of earth
ESCAPE VELOCITY—1.48 miles per second

The stack accelerated rapidly, losing weight at the rate of almost 30,000 pounds every second as the engines gulped their propellants. In half a minute the vehicle was moving faster than the sound of its engines, and in the Command Module, a football-field-length removed from the engine nozzles, it was quiet. Armstrong, Aldrin, and Collins, pushed deep in their couches by the force of acceleration, were for the time being only monitors, watching their displays for indications of trouble, reporting their observations to mission control in Houston.

At an altitude of 27 miles, the first stage's center engine cut off, on schedule to the tenth of a second. The digital clock in the cabin showed 2 minutes 15 seconds GET; GET is Ground Elapsed Time, or the time since liftoff.

Twenty-five seconds later the four outboard engines shut down. The S-IC stage had completed its assignment of boosting the stack to an altitude of 41 miles and to a speed of 6,150 miles per hour. The Instrument Unit triggered detonation of the explosive charges which separated the stage and touched off the retrofiring solid rockets which insure clearance.

The remaining stack coasted for two seconds, lightened by three-quarters of the pad weight with the loss of S-IC and the consumption of its propellants. There was another brief rocket burst: this time it was the ullage engines firing to settle S-II's fuel and oxidizer in their tanks. Almost instantly, the five engines of the second stage ignited.

Now driven by the million-plus pounds of thrust of the second-stage propulsion system, the stack arced over the Atlantic toward Africa. Steering was handled by the brainy Instrument Unit, whose guidance system was comparing actual path with desired path and making them coincide by proper gimballing of the engines. The launch escape tower, no longer needed, was jettisoned. This gave the astronauts their first good look at space. Until now, the conical sheath which protected the Command Module from exit heating had covered four of the five windows, but the ejected tower took the sheath with it.

After a burn of slightly less than 6½ minutes, the second stage engines shut down. Separation was again initiated, and S-II departed the stack, having rocketed the vehicle to an altitude of 115 miles and a velocity of about 15,000 miles per hour.

Once more there was a brief coasting period and an ullage maneuver; then the S-IVB stage's single J-2 engine took over the propulsion job. It fired for 2 minutes 25 seconds while the Instrument Unit guided the abbreviated stack toward the imaginary doughnut-hole in the sky that was the narrow entryway to the precise orbit planned. At 11 minutes 50 seconds Ground Elapsed Time, the flow of propellants to the engine was cut off. S-IVB did not drop away; it coasted with Apollo 11, traveling at close to 17,500 miles per hour in an orbit 117 miles high.

The Jump Out of Earth Orbit

The next revolution and a half was a busy time for everyone as the astronauts, their supporters on the ground, and the almost-human Instrument Unit made preparations for the big leap into deep space. Armstrong, Aldrin, and Collins tested all of the spacecraft's systems, double-checked by mission control, whose computer was collecting, processing, and displaying telemetered data on Apollo's condition. Each of the tracking stations was making its contribution to the information bank, relaying it to Houston and thence to the Instrument Unit.

The jump out of earth orbit, called the *translunar injection*, was a maneuver demanding utmost precision. The first requirement was additional velocity. This would permit the spacecraft to escape earth orbit, although it would not completely escape gravity; throughout most of the flight earth's mass would continue to exert some gravitational influence. The velocity needed was roughly 24,500 miles per hour, or an increase of about 7,000 miles per hour above orbital speed. Its attainment depended upon a precisely timed restart and second burn of the single J-2 engine on the S-IVB third stage.

Another requirement was exact aiming of the spacecraft at the moment the burn was initiated. For this flight, mission control wanted a *free-return trajectory*. "Free return" means that the path would take Apollo on a big figure-eight around the moon and back to earth even if the spacecraft engine became inoperable; changing earth and lunar gravity conditions would dictate the flight course, and final adjustment for earth re-entry could be made by Apollo's small thrusters.

Obviously, Apollo 11 was not aimed directly at the moon, because the moon was moving around the earth, and it would travel some 150,000 miles in the time it would take the spacecraft to reach lunar distance. So, like a skeet-shooter leading his target, the computer directed Apollo to a point in space where the moon would be three days later.

The third requirement was determination of where and when to start the burn. Clearly, hitting the target demanded accurate establishment of the starting point. The starting point was an imaginary bullseye, called the *translunar injection window*. Were the window a fixed point determinable by earth landmark, the task would have been a simple one. But

THE ASTRONAUTS OF APOLLO 11

Neil Alden Armstrong,
Commander

Civilian

Astronaut since Sept., 1962

Born: Aug. 5, 1930,
Wapakoneta, Ohio

Purdue University,
Bachelor's degree in
    aeronautical engineering

Previous space flight:
Gemini 8

Michael Collins,
Command Module Pilot

Lieutenant Colonel,
    U.S. Air Force

Astronaut since Oct., 1963

Born: Oct. 31, 1930,
Rome, Italy

U.S. Military Academy,
Bachelor of Science

Previous space flight:
Gemini 10

Edwin Eugene Aldrin, Jr.,
Lunar Module Pilot

Colonel, U.S. Air Force

Astronaut since Oct., 1963

Born: Jan. 20, 1930,
Glen Ridge, New Jersey

U.S. Military Academy;
Massachusetts Institute of
    Technology, Doctor of
    Science degree in
    astronautics

Previous space flight:
Gemini 12

it was not. Both the moon and the earth were in motion, so the window also moved.

Translunar injection, then, added up to this: the space vehicle had to be guided through the window at a given split-second, the engine burn had to begin at exactly that instant, the spacecraft had to be precisely aimed at burn-start, and the engine had to operate for a specific period of time.

The Instrument Unit had an important collaborator for the monumental task of injection. The supercomputer at Houston compared the relative positions of Apollo 11, earth, moon, and launch window, performed all the calculations incident to proper trajectory, then "fed" the Instrument Unit. That computer steered the stack to the bullseye, nudged the spacecraft into correct attitude, and triggered the J-2's ignition.

Translunar injection started over the mid-Pacific at 2 hours 44 minutes Ground Elapsed Time. A burn of just under 6 minutes provided the requisite trajectory and velocity. Apollo 11 was en route to the moon.

Restacking for the Journey

Coasting in moonbound path, the astronauts "sat tight" for 10 minutes, giving the ground stations time to establish the new track. Then it was time for the *turnaround*, the maneuver designed to bring together the basic spacecraft—code-named *Columbia* for the Apollo 11 mission—and the Lunar Module, or *Eagle*.

The astronauts first triggered a set of explosive charges that blew away the walls of *Eagle's* temporary "garage," the four panels of the Lunar Module Adapter. Then, with Collins handling the small thrusters of the Service Module, the basic spacecraft flew about 100 feet from the Lunar Module, turned around and jockeyed to a docking. The probe in the Command Module slipped into the Lunar Module's drogue, a spring mechanism pulled the two spacecraft tightly together, and 12 latches in the probe system locked and sealed the hatches of each module. The hatches now formed a tunnel permitting movement from one module to the other.

At this point, a powerful spring mechanism freed the Lunar Module from the S-IVB stage. Firing reverse thrust, Collins backed away from the S-IVB, and Apollo 11 was in three-module lunar configuration.

S-IVB and the Instrument Unit were no longer needed; the astronauts bade them good-bye with a short burst of thrust from the main engine that moved Apollo into a slightly different flight path. At a signal from earth, the remaining propellants in the S-IVB were dumped through the engine.

Even without burning, the high-speed flow of liquid imparted a slight thrust to the stage, enough to take it well away from Apollo 11's trajectory. The vehicles would move farther and farther apart as the mission progressed, until S-IVB and the Instrument Unit passed behind the trailing edge of the moon and went into solar orbit.

With the departure of the Instrument Unit, *Columbia's* own guidance and navigation system took over the brainwork, while the main Apollo engine replaced the J-2 as the muscle element of the team. The attitude changes made earlier by the S-IVB's small reaction motors would henceforth be handled by the 16 thrusters ringing the Service Module. They could tilt the spacecraft in any desired position for a variety of purposes: better visibility, photography, course corrections, aiming the optical sighting system at a particular star, or pointing the deep-space antenna toward earth.

Soon after lunar trajectory had been achieved, the crewmen took off their cumbersome, restrictive, 35-pound spacesuits. The suits supply breathing oxygen, pressure, and air conditioning when they are needed, but they are worn only during the critical phases of a mission—launch and operations near the moon. The rest of the time the Apollo astronauts wear a simple lightweight flight coverall. In the unlikely event that a micrometeoroid puncture should spring a leak in the pressurized cabin, the environmental system would automatically pump harder to compensate. It would lose the battle, but it would provide the astronauts 15 minutes in which to don and plug in the spacesuits. The suits would be able to support life in a decompressed cabin for as much as 115 hours, long enough for a return to earth from any point in a lunar mission.

Shortly after the start of the moonbound coasting period, Collins initiated *thermal control,* the barbeque-like rolling action that insures uniform heat distribution over the spacecraft's exterior. The roll was to continue throughout the mission except during star-sighting and course corrections and the time in lunar orbit.

The Long Coast to the Moon

As Apollo 11 moved farther into space, the earth-sphere rapidly diminished in size and the sight of the globe, partially cloud-covered and bluish-green against the inky background of the universe, awed the astronauts as it had their predecessors. Armstrong demonstrated his ability as cloud interpreter, one of the many skills astronauts acquire in the course of their intensive training program. Noting the cloud circulation around Houston,

Even men on the way to the moon are fascinated by the receding earth. In one of the best pictures ever taken of our planet, the Mediterranean Sea shows very deep blue, with Africa looming large and orange-rust beneath it.

he ventured the opinion that it was raining there. It was. But, because he could see that the trailing edge of the storm cloud was just approaching Houston, Armstrong added that "it looks like it ought to clear up pretty soon." The storm ended less than half an hour later.

"Fantastic"—a word that has become a standard part of the Apollo lexicon—was the way the astronauts described their view of the receding earth. Aldrin also reported that, while the bluish-green coloring predominated, shadings in different parts of the earth were clearly noticeable. The United Kingdom, he said, was "definitely greener" than the Spanish peninsula, which he described as "brownish-green."

The lunar trajectory into which Apollo 11 had been thrust called for an en route time of 73 hours (on other missions it might range from 60 to 100 hours). This might seem a long time to the earthling, but to Armstrong, Aldrin, and Collins it was anything but monotonous.

The process of making sure that all systems were working as they should was continual. Communication with mission control had to be maintained. Constant updating of the onboard computer, with information supplied by earth stations, was necessary. The crew had to navigate by sighting stars or earth landmarks; radar tracking stations on earth were providing the primary navigational calculations, but the crew had to be prepared for the possibility of a loss of contact with earth, in which case their sightings would become the only method of guiding the craft. Sleeping and eating consumed a good part of the time, and public interest demanded a number of TV transmissions to earth.

Normally, considerable time would have been spent preparing for and executing mid-course corrections. Even a slight error at injection would have been multiplied over the great distance the spacecraft must travel, so the flight plan allowed for as many as four course alterations during the trip to the moon.

On Apollo missions, it is the job of the guidance computer to decide how far the spacecraft is off the optimum course and to direct the correction. Since speed is the factor that dictates a space flight path, course changes are made by increasing or decreasing velocity; the computer determines the required application of thrust. If a large correction is needed, the energy is supplied by a brief burn of the main engine; minute corrections can be made by the thrusters, conserving the big engine's fuel.

On Apollo 11, however, the initial aiming was so precise as to almost negate the need for mid-course corrections. Collins made only one, some 24 hours after translunar injection, and it was a very minor one.

As Apollo 11 moved farther from earth, its velocity dropped sharply. It was like the long uphill climb of a powerless vehicle. Earth's gravity was still an influence tending to restrain the spacecraft's departure by canceling some of its momentum. In the first 20,000 miles, the slowing effect had reduced Apollo 11's speed from the initial 24,500 to about 10,000 miles per hour. At 80,000 miles, velocity was down to less than 5,000 miles per hour, and at 150,000 miles, it was a shade under 3,000 miles per hour. However, earth gravity's influence was weakening as the distance from the planet increased.

At 62 hours 40 minutes Ground Elapsed Time, when Apollo 11 had moved more than 200,000 miles from earth, some five-sixths of the way to the moon, velocity was down to little more than 2,000 miles per hour. But earth gravity had given up the fight; its influence at this distance was negligible.

A Satellite of the Moon

Now, however, a new gravitational force came into play. The moon, swinging in its orbit toward the intercept point, was only 30,000 miles away, and lunar gravity "captured" Apollo 11. It bent the flight path toward the moon and gradually increased spacecraft velocity until it reached 5,700 miles per hour.

At 74 hours 50 minutes Ground Elapsed Time, an hour from the point of lunar intercept, Armstrong, Aldrin, and Collins began preparations for the first of the supercritical maneuvers, the *insertion into lunar orbit*. Apollo 11 was exactly on course for the target point, but it was moving too rapidly. As is the case in sending an object into earth orbit, lunar orbit demands a balance between gravity and the centrifugal force of space-craft velocity. But moon gravity is only one-sixth that of earth's, and velocity requirements are correspondingly lower. For the 70-mile-high orbit the Apollo 11 astronauts wanted, the counterbalancing force translated into 3,600 miles per hour. In other words, Apollo 11's speed of 5,700 miles per hour had to be reduced by 2,100 miles per hour to effect proper orbit.

As a first step, Command Module pilot Collins reoriented the spacecraft's attitude so that the exhaust nozzle of the main engine was pointed forward along the line of flight. In this attitude, engine thrust would produce a braking action rather than an acceleration. Updated by its hyperintelligent colleague at Houston, the onboard computer determined when to fire the engine and precisely how long a burn would be needed for the necessary velocity subtraction. Then, at 75 hours 50 minutes Ground Elapsed Time, it actuated the valves controlling propellant flow, and the engine rumbled into action.

This was a supercritical maneuver because an improper burn could create situations ranging from serious hazard to improper orbit; no burn at all would swing Apollo 11 around the moon and back toward earth, aborting the landing phase of the mission. It was a tense, nerve-wracking period for mission-followers on earth, because the burn took place behind the moon, on the side away from earth, where communication was blocked by the moon's mass.

But it went, as Collins reported, "like perfect." A 5-minute 57-second burn sent Apollo 11 into an elliptical orbit around the moon reaching as high as 196 miles, then dipping back to 70 miles.

For the maneuvers to follow, however, the Apollo 11 crew wanted a circular orbit in which the basic spacecraft—Columbia—would remain at a constant altitude. So, after two revolutions in the elliptical orbit, they again fired the main engine, making a fine adjustment in velocity which "circularized" the orbit.

There followed an 11-revolution coasting period during which the astronauts conducted another series of systems checks and confirmed their orbital path by sighting on lunar landmarks. The thousands of photos provided by Ranger, Surveyor, and Lunar Orbiter had produced a detailed lunar atlas, and the Apollo 11 crew, from long training, were at least as familiar with the moon's surface as they were with earth's. The earth tracking stations, locked onto Apollo 11 during the "visible" portion of the orbit, also relayed orbital data to the onboard computer, and their exact path and landing approach was calculated.

The Service Module casting its shadow on the moon, the astronauts received their first view of the approach to Landing Site 2 (in the center near the edge of darkness) while still docked. The rill in the upper left was called U.S.1. Crater Moltke, one of their major landmarks, is to the right of it. Diamondback Rill extends across the middle.

The Final Distance to the Moon

With concurrence from mission control, the astronauts proceeded to the main event—the lunar landing. On the 11th revolution, Armstrong and Aldrin entered and powered up the Lunar Module, an operation more complicated than it sounds.

First, the Lunar Module and the connecting tunnel had to be pressurized from oxygen supplies in the Service Module. Then Collins removed the hatch on the Command Module's end of the tunnel. Armstrong unlatched the docking fittings and removed the tunnel-blocking probe and drogue, passing them to Collins for temporary stowage. The moonmen crawled through the tunnel, closing the Lunar Module hatch behind them, and activated the craft's equipment. They ran through the lengthy process of checking out all systems for this hitherto-unused spacecraft, concluding by extending the landing legs. Collins, now solo in the Command Module, replaced the probe and drogue and closed the hatch in his cabin. From this point until the docking some 28 hours later Apollo 11 would be two separate spacecraft—*Columbia* and *Eagle*.

At 100 hours 15 minutes Ground Elapsed Time, a spring mechanism separated the two spacecraft, and the moonbound astronauts fired a short burst from the Lunar Module's thrusters, taking *Eagle* about 50 feet from *Columbia.* Maintaining this distance while flying formation in orbit, the crew of *Eagle* performed a number of attitude changes to check out their thrusters and to permit Collins, in *Columbia,* to perform a complete visual inspection of the Lunar Module.

Then came the second supercritical step, the initial descent from the 70-mile orbit to a point 50,000 feet above the surface. The flight path was not simply a fall toward the moon but actually a new orbit in which, had the astronauts for any reason elected not to continue the descent when they reached 50,000 feet, *Eagle* would have swung upward without power and returned to *Columbia's* orbital altitude. The new orbit was attained by a half-minute brief firing of the Lunar Module's descent engine, used for the first time on the mission. The engine's braking thrust took the Lunar Module out of its original path and directed it toward Landing Site Number Two in the Sea of Tranquillity, the spot destined to be man's first port of call on the moon.

Through about half a revolution, *Eagle* dropped toward the surface, accelerating until it was moving at 4,600 miles per hour as it approached the 50,000-foot level. This was another decision plateau; five seconds before *Eagle* reached 50,000 feet, a light began to flash on the console. The computer was, in effect, "asking" the astronauts if they wanted to go ahead with the third supercritical event, the final approach and touchdown. Armstrong replied by punching the "proceed" button. Computer-directed, the descent engine roared into action.

Eagle's computer, the third electronic brain to go into action since launch from earth, was one of several new systems brought into play during the descent. Not used on the moonbound flight, it now took over *Eagle's* guidance and control function, automatically performing the maneuvers except when Armstrong and Aldrin chose to fly the craft manually. A second, backup computer followed every move of *Eagle* in case an emergency demanded its use.

Keeping the moonbug stable was the job of the Lunar Module's 16 small thrusters; the guidance system determined which of them should be fired and for how long. The computer was assisted by the landing radar, which continually measured *Eagle's* altitude, velocity, the angle to the touchdown point, and the distance from it. All of this information, computer-processed and translated into display form, appeared on a screen in the crew compartment.

West Crater loomed up on
their left . . .

. . . and then slid from view
as *Eagle* moved on.

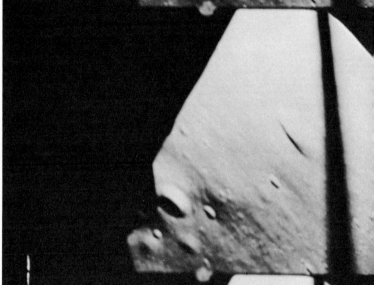

Dust was kicked up by the
engine's exhaust . . . the
Eagle had landed. Latitude
0° 38′ 50″. Longitude 23°
30′ 17″. July 20, 1969, as
earth reckons time.

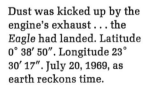

Thanks to Armstrong's quick maneuver away from a boulder field, *Eagle's* landing site was in a flat area. Only small rocks and pits on the still-untouched surface were visible through the right-hand window of the landing craft.

The descent was in three phases. First came the *braking phase,* in which the engine operated at high thrust to subtract most of *Eagle's* velocity. During this period, which covered close to 300 miles over the surface, speed dropped to about 60 miles per hour, and the craft descended to an altitude of 7,000 feet.

Oddly, during this critical phase, Armstrong and Aldrin could not see the moon at all. The Lunar Module was in an almost horizontal attitude with the fore section of the module—the part with the windows—facing upward. In other words, Armstrong and Aldrin were almost on their backs, staring through the windows into the void of space. At 7,000 feet, however, they entered the *visibility phase;* the spacecraft pitched over to a more upright angle, and the astronauts got their first close look at the moon. At that point, the landing radar was reporting that the touchdown site was only 5 miles away.

About half a mile from the touchdown point, *Eagle* went into the *landing phase.* Its thrusters adjusted attitude so that the Lunar Module was practically vertical, descending on a column of rocket thrust. The engine at this point was producing about 2,800 pounds of thrust, all that was required since *Eagle* had become some 8 tons lighter during the descent by virtue of fuel consumed. Altitude was 500 feet, and *Eagle* was sinking slowly like a helicopter.

Suddenly Armstrong grabbed the throttle and wrested control of the spacecraft from the computer. The computer had been doing its job perfectly, aiming for a predetermined spot on the moon. But that spot, Armstrong and Aldrin saw as they got their first good look at it, was in a football-field-sized crater whose floor was strewn with huge boulders!

Armstrong applied power to halt the descent and fired the thrusters to move sideways. The thrust application took *Eagle* a half-mile past the crater, where Armstrong found an even-surfaced area. The brief moment of crisis was over so quickly no one at Houston knew it had happened.

Armstrong eased off on the throttle and started a new descent—50, 40, 30 feet. At 20 feet *Eagle* was dropping at only 3 feet per second, about the speed of a very slow elevator. Fifteen feet, 10. A blue light flashed on the console, telling the crew that the landing probes had touched; *Eagle* was only 5½ feet from the surface. Armstrong quickly killed the engine to minimize the rocket-induced dust storm, and *Eagle* settled gently onto the moon, its shock-absorbing legs cushioning the impact.

"Tranquillity Base Here"

"The *Eagle* has landed," Armstrong calmly reported to Houston and to several hundred million tense televiewers. Ground Elapsed Time was 102 hours 45 minutes.

It was the greatest and most dramatic moment in human history, heightened by the fact that people all over the world could share the experience through the medium of television. An age-old dream had been fulfilled; man had landed on another celestial body and inaugurated an epoch of extraterrestrial travel.

The moonscape was awe-inspiring. From the windows of the Lunar Module, the crew of *Eagle* looked out on a monotonous wasteland pocked by craters and pimpled by rocks. The fabled mountains of the moon were nowhere in evidence; Landing Site Number Two had been selected because it was comfortably removed from the potentially troublesome peaks, and the curvature of the moon was so sharp that the horizon was less than two miles distant. The sun hung low on the horizon, casting long and very dark shadows on the surface. Because there were no atmospheric molecules to give it color, the lunar sky was inky black.

"Magnificent desolation!" Aldrin described it. In their first transmissions from "Tranquillity Base," the new designation for the touchdown point, the men of *Eagle* had this to say of their first look at the moon.

Aldrin: "It's pretty much without color. It's gray, and it's very white— chalky gray as you look into the zero phase line (toward the sun) and it's considerably darker gray, more like ash, ashen gray, as you look 90 degrees to the sun."

Armstrong: "There is a relatively level plain cratered with a fairly large number of craters of the 5 to 50 foot variety, and some ridges, small, 20-30 feet high, I would guess. And literally thousands of little one and 2-foot craters around the area. We see some angular blocks several hundred feet in front of us that are probably 2 feet in size and have angular edges. There is a hill in view just about on the ground track ahead of us. Difficult to estimate, but it might be half a mile or a mile."

Eager to move out onto the lunar surface, Armstrong and Aldrin got mission control's okay to skip the lengthy rest period called for by the Apollo book. There still remained, however, a number of very important and time-consuming preliminaries.

First item on the agenda was checkout of the ascent stage, which took 2 hours. Next, the *Eagle* crew "unstowed" the environmental backpacks to be worn on the surface and subjected them to an intensive inspection. Then they began to struggle laboriously into their extravehicular suits.

Over the regular pressure suit, they donned the nine-layered protective thermal outer garment with its specially-designed lunar boots and gloves. They fitted the double-shelled extravehicular visor, which would afford protection from sunglare and micrometeoroids, over the regular plastic pressure helmet, sealing the connections at the neck ring.

They strapped on the backpacks, turned them on, and conducted another careful check, with mission control watching via telemetry. Everything was go, so as a last step they depressurized the crew compartment; if the hatch were opened while the module was at full pressure, *Eagle* would implode, or collapse inward.

Leaving Footprints on the Moon

Armstrong started down the nine-rung ladder. Near the top he paused to pull a lanyard; this popped open the equipment bay on the exterior of the descent stage, where much of the equipment needed on the surface was

Neil Armstrong, clothed in a protective suit and carrying oxygen supplies on his back, stepped through the hatch and out on to *Eagle's* ladder.

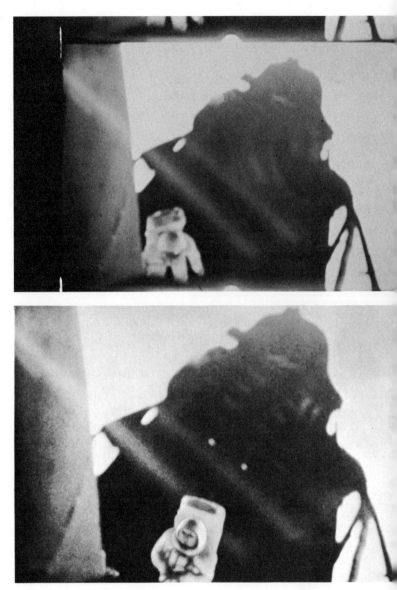

And he became the first man to set foot on another celestial body, opening a new era of human history.

stowed. Among the equipment was a tiny, 7½-pound TV camera already focused on the foot of the landing ladder. Some 600,000,000 people on earth thrilled to the view as Armstrong slowly descended and stepped onto the surface of the moon, saying as he did so, "That's one small step for a man, one giant leap for mankind." The step came at 109 hours 24 minutes Ground Elapsed Time.

The lunar boot stepping onto the moon's surface left prints
in the powdery dust which no rain can wash away nor wind
cover over. The Apollo 11 astronauts had changed the face
of the moon forever.

But Armstrong did not pause to relish the drama of the moment. He
started immediately on his assigned tasks. First he did a series of easy
exercises to become accustomed to movement in the moon's one-sixth
gravity. The pressure in his suit kept Armstrong from bending over or
reaching his arms above his head, but he reported that movement was
easier than anticipated.

Within a few minutes of his first step, Armstrong was gamboling about
the surface like a lunar veteran, awkward-looking in his bulky costume
but covering ground easily and gracefully with a long, springy stride. With
spacesuit, outer garments, and backpack contributing 183 pounds, Armstrong's overall weight was up to almost 350 earth pounds. His lunar
weight, however, was only 58 pounds.

Next, using a special scoop carried in the equipment bay, Armstrong
dug a "contingency sample" of lunar soil, in case an emergency prevented
completion of the more inclusive sample collection planned.

Eighteen minutes after Armstrong, Aldrin became the second man on
the moon. After his exercise period, he joined Armstrong at the foot of the
Lunar Module ladder and the two unveiled a plaque affixed to the landing

leg. To be left behind to commemorate man's first visit, it was signed by Armstrong, Aldrin, Collins, and President Richard M. Nixon, and it read:

HERE MEN FROM THE PLANET EARTH
FIRST SET FOOT UPON THE MOON
JULY 1969 A.D.
WE CAME IN PEACE FOR ALL MANKIND

Armstrong took the camera from the equipment bay and treated the televiewing world to a panoramic view of the moon, shooting toward the horizon through several different points of the compass. Then he mounted the camera on a tripod some 40 feet from the Lunar Module; it would automatically transmit TV pictures for the remainder of the visit.

Aldrin, meanwhile, had set up the first of three scientific experiments, a "window shade" made of aluminum foil. Extended full length on a rod, the shade was designed to trap the *solar wind*, not a wind in the accepted sense of the word but an invisible cloud composed of tiny fragments of material ejected from the sun. Later, scientists on earth would carefully analyze the "catch" in an effort to determine what gases or particles make up the solar wind.

Both moonmen then erected a 3-by-5-foot American flag, fixed to keep it unfurled in the airless lunar environment. Armstrong and Aldrin stood at attention near the flag as President Nixon, in the first telephone call to the moon, congratulated them on their "immense feat."

After the ceremony, the lunar explorers filled the first of their two rock boxes with a *bulk sample*, 35 pounds of soil and rock dug from one area near the Lunar Module.

The greatest distance ventured from the Lunar Module was about 200 feet, attained by Armstrong when he "took a stroll," as he later put it. He took a first-hand look at a fair-sized crater—"maybe 70 or 80 feet in diameter and 15 or 20 feet deep. It had rocks on the bottom that were bigger than anything on the surface and I took quite a few pictures of them." He made the photos with a still camera.

Armstrong and Aldrin then proceeded to make a visual inspection of the exterior of the Lunar Module, noting in particular the depth to which the landing legs had dipped into the surface (2 to 3 inches) and the effect of rocket blast on the lunar soil.

The inspection completed, the inhabitants of Tranquillity Base opened

Astronaut Aldrin joined the picture-taking Armstrong on the
bright, white surface, which Aldrin described as "magnificent
desolation." Together the men planted the American flag on
the moon, and then began their exploration of the landing
site. With the foil-covered *Eagle* and the photographer
reflected in his gold visor, Aldrin posed against the lunar
horizon, looking like science fiction come true.

Things they left behind them on the moon: equipment for
the benefit of scientists on earth, and a 1½-inch silicon disc
carrying messages of goodwill from more than 70 leaders
of Earth's nations. The messages (samples shown below)
were photographically reduced in size 200 times and etched
on to the disc by a process used in making microcircuits.

Things they took with them from the moon: rock samples of as many types as they could find, plus numerous photographs of the lunar surface, and tired but happy smiles. Pioneer moon-walker Armstrong finally had his photograph taken, too, after he and Aldrin returned to *Eagle* and pressurized it for a well-deserved rest before liftoff.

another bay in the Lunar Module descent stage and unstowed the remaining two scientific experiments.

Moving some 70 feet from the Lunar Module to insure that the later rocket blast would not damage the equipment, Aldrin set up the seismic station, a battery of four seismometers that register moonquakes with which scientists hope to attain a better understanding of the lunar structure. With its own transmitter and power supply, the station was designed to operate after the astronauts' return to earth.

Armstrong, meanwhile, had mounted the last experiment, a laser reflector. Built of cubes of silica, the reflector acts like a mirror, bouncing laser beams directed from earth back to their points of origin. Measurements of the round-trip time can provide extremely precise data on earthmoon distances, moon size, earth's rotation, and the rate at which earth's continents are drifting apart. Within minutes of the time Armstrong erected the device, an earth station reported the first laser contact.

Nearing the end of his allotted time on the surface, Aldrin had one more task. With a coring device which he hammered 5 inches into the moonsoil, he took two subsurface *core samples*. Then, rolling up the solar wind experiment and taking it with him, he re-entered the Lunar Module.

Alone on the surface, Armstrong hastily started on an assignment which was to have been collection of a box of "documented" samples, photographed and tagged as to time and location of pickup. But mission control wanted a generous safety margin and had set a time limit for operation of the life-support backpack. With only a few minutes left, Armstrong glided about gathering as many different varieties of rock as he could find, reporting at last that he had "about 20 pounds of carefully selected if not documented samples."

Armstrong used his remaining time to send up to Aldrin in the Lunar Module, via conveyor line, the two precious rock boxes and a film pack from the still camera. Everything else, 30 items of equipment worth more than $1,000,000, was to be left behind on the moon because of weight and contamination considerations.

As tokens of their contributions to space progress, Armstrong left the medals of five spacemen: the Soviet Union's Yuri Gagarin, the first man in space, later killed in a plane crash; Vladimir Komarov, the Soviet cosmonaut who lost his life in the fouled-parachute descent of the Soyuz 1 spacecraft in 1967; and Virgil Grissom, Edward White, and Roger Chaffee, Apollo astronauts who died in the tragic fire of January, 1967. Armstrong also left on the moon an Apollo 11 insignia—an eagle holding an olive branch—symbolic of the United States' peaceful intent in lunar exploration. Finally, he deposited on the surface a small disc containing micro-filmed messages from 70 world leaders.

His last chore completed, Armstrong mounted the ladder, squeezed through the hatch, and closed it behind him. Man's first walk on the moon had ended, at 111 hours 40 minutes Ground Elapsed Time.

Return to "Columbia"

The *Eagle* crewmen repressurized the spacecraft, divested themselves of the bulky extravehicular suits and backpacks (dropping them to the lunar surface, too), checked systems again, had a quick meal, then curled up in

The ascent stage of *Eagle* lifted off from its launch platform with perfect ease to rejoin the circling *Columbia* where Michael Collins had kept his lonely vigil in an orbit 70 miles above his moon-walking colleagues.

the corners of the spacecraft for a well-deserved rest. At 121 hours Ground Elapsed Time, after seven hours of fitful sleep, they started preparations for the fourth supercritical operation of the mission, the lunar liftoff.

The ascent preparations began with the inevitable all-systems check and a lengthy communication with Collins, still orbiting at 70 miles in the Command Module. *Eagle's* computer, together with *Columbia's,* was updated by Houston. The Lunar Module's rendezvous radar was activated, and it began tracking *Columbia* during the time when it was electronically visible. Armstrong and Aldrin monitored their displays while the computer decided the proper split-second for launch; timing is always essential in Apollo flights, but it is particularly so in lunar liftoffs, because the goal is not simply attainment of orbit but insertion into a very precise orbit compatible with that of the basic spacecraft.

Aside from the moon landing, the lunar liftoff was the most critical of all the major steps, because the engine, though thoroughly tested on earth, had never before been fired in the lunar environment. Armstrong and Aldrin were literally betting their lives on the performance of the ascent engine; if it failed, they were stranded on the moon. There were no surface rescue provisions; Collins in the Command Module could descend to 50,000 feet to effect a rescue, but that was his lower limit, and the ascent engine would have to burn 7 minutes to send *Eagle* to that altitude.

Liftoff! At 124 hours 22 minutes Ground Elapsed Time the ascent engine, smallest of all the main propulsion systems in the Saturn V/Apollo stack, ignited to produce a constant 3,500 pounds thrust. Simultaneously, explosive charges broke the connections mating the ascent stage to the descent stage, which was now a launch platform. The truncated *Eagle* climbed straight up, moving slowly at first, then accelerating. For 7 minutes 14 seconds the engine burned, boosting *Eagle* to a speed of nearly 4,000 miles per hour, sufficient for a low-altitude lunar orbit. At 10 miles, *Eagle* pitched over and went into an elliptical orbit with a high point of 55 miles. Upon reaching that altitude, Armstrong fired his small thrusters briefly to increase speed slightly and to circularize his orbit.

At this point, 125 hours 21 minutes into the mission, the two spacecraft were in concentric circular orbits, *Eagle* some 15 miles below *Columbia* and trailing behind the basic spacecraft—but because it was lower it was also moving faster, hence gradually catching up. Through slightly more than one revolution, while the rendezvous radar kept track of *Columbia's* position, *Eagle* gradually narrowed the distance by its greater speed, while at the same time Armstrong closed the altitude gap by a series of firings of his thrusters. It was time for the fifth of the supercritical steps.

With a final short burst from his thrusters, Armstrong nudged the Lunar Module into a position nose-to-nose with the Command Module and only 20 feet from it. Then Collins took over the docking duties. Sighting on a target reference on the Lunar Module, he jockeyed *Columbia* the remaining distance. The probe engaged the drogue, and the two modules were locked together. *Eagle* and *Columbia* were once again Apollo 11. Ground Elapsed Time was 128 hours 4 minutes.

Armstrong and Aldrin remained in the Lunar Module for more than an hour after docking; the transfers took that long. First, the hatch had to be pressurized, and the probe and drogue removed. Then Armstrong and Aldrin passed through the tunnel to Collins the invaluable moon samples, the film, and certain other equipment to be brought back to earth. Collins then transferred to the Lunar Module everything in his compartment no longer required. Armstrong and Aldrin crawled through the tunnel and sealed the hatch. Finally, proud *Eagle,* first vehicle to carry men to the moon, was abandoned. No longer needed, its flimsy structure unable to survive earth re-entry, it was jettisoned unceremoniously in lunar orbit.

Back to Earth

Together again in their Command Module couches, the Apollo 11 trio had a brief rest before it was time for the sixth supercritical step, the departure from the moon, or *transearth injection.*

Like the push that started Apollo toward the moon several days earlier, transearth injection required a speed increase. Apollo 11 was moving at one mile a second, or 3,600 miles per hour. Escape from lunar orbit demanded a velocity of at least 5,400 miles per hour. But, for Apollo 11, the mission planners had selected a fast, 60-hour homebound path, and for the desired trajectory a velocity of 5,700 miles per hour was needed. The guidance computer decided that this would take a main engine burn of 2 minutes 29 seconds. The burn was an absolute *must;* if the engine failed to fire, or if it fired too briefly to attain escape velocity, Apollo 11 could not get out of orbit because its small thrusters did not have the necessary power.

But, as it proved, there was no need to worry about what might have happened. The departure went the way of the rest of the mission—flawlessly. At 135 hours 25 minutes Ground Elapsed Time, while the spacecraft was behind the moon and out of contact with earth, the engine fired and acceleration began. By the time *Columbia* emerged from the back side it was already in its transearth path.

The return voyage followed the pattern of the outbound trip: continual systems checks, the slow roll for thermal control, constant updating of the guidance system by means of astronaut navigation and earth-provided data, and two TV transmissions to earth.

Mid-course corrections were practically non-existent. Fifteen hours from the moon Collins made a brief firing of the thrusters, making such a slight velocity change that it was more properly a course refinement than a correction. And, as it turned out, that was to be the last trajectory adjustment.

In the reverse of the outbound path, Apollo 11 slowed initially after the moon-departure, dropping to a minimum velocity of about 2,500 miles per hour. Then, when earth's gravity "reacquired" the spacecraft, speed began to pick up. The rate of increase was very slow in the early stages; 100,000 miles from the moon, velocity was still under 4,000 miles per hour. But in the final stages of the return, as earth's pull became stronger, speed went up sharply. Fourteen thousand miles from re-entry, Apollo 11 was moving at 11,000 miles per hour. Just 40 minutes later, only 5,000 miles out, it traveling at 17,000 miles per hour and accelerating at a very rapid rate.

The last of the supercritical steps was about to get under way. Two earlier manned returns from lunar orbit had made the re-entry seem easy, but it was, nonetheless, a hazardous step, not only for the precision guidance demanded but also because of the complete dependency on the landing system.

The target was an imaginary rectangular slot 400,000 feet above earth's surface. This altitude represented the threshold of atmosphere, where *Columbia* would encounter the first thinly spread air molecules, hence the start of friction heating. The slot was approximately 28 miles wide and in its other dimension it was 2 degrees deep, meaning that the spacecraft had only that much leeway in the angle at which it crossed the threshold. A re-entry on the low side of the slot would subject the astronauts to crushing forces of deceleration and friction temperatures beyond the limits of the heat shield. An overshoot would cause the spacecraft to bounce back into inescapable earth orbit.

But there were no re-entry problems for Apollo; that maneuver, like all the others, went "like perfect."

It began at 194 hours 49 minutes Ground Elapsed Time. The Service Module had completed the last of its assignments, and Collins touched off explosive charges to jettison it. The Service Module's thrusters were fired to move it safely away from the Command Module; unshielded, the Service Module would plunge to destruction in the atmosphere. Of the eight-

Surrounded by the footprints that Neil Armstrong and Edwin Aldrin had made in the lunar dust, the American flag was left standing alone when the astronauts departed. The flag does not claim the moon for the United States, but it does proclaim the moon to be a scientific preserve for mankind.

segment, 3,200-ton stack that had departed Cape Kennedy's launch pad eight days earlier, only the Command Module remained.

Nose toward earth until this point, the Command Module was turned around by a brief firing of its own thrusters, never before used on the mission. Now foremost was the blunt bottom, both the primary heat shield and the lift-creating "wing" for descent control.

Ground Elapsed Time 195 hours 3 minutes. At 24,678 miles per hour, *Columbia* plunged through the slot into earth's layer of atmosphere. As the air became progressively more dense, atmospheric drag slowed the space-craft abruptly. Armstrong, Aldrin, and Collins experienced a deceleration force of about 6½ G's, uncomfortable but well within tolerable limits. A miles-long tongue of fire trailed the spacecraft, whose heat shield reached

Re-entry . . . splashdown . . . and the beginning of isolation
for the astronauts before the world could welcome them.
Wearing their biological isolation garments, they awaited
pickup by a helicopter from the USS *Hornet*.

APOLLO 11 MISSION EVENTS

EVENT	GROUND ELAPSED TIME*	EVENT	GROUND ELAPSED TIME*
Launch and earth orbit phase		Command Module/Lunar Module	
Launch (first motion)	00.00.00	separation	100.15
First-stage center engine cutoff	00.02.15	Start of final approach to moon	102.33
First-stage outboard engine cutoff	00.02.40	*Eagle's* touchdown on moon	102.45
Second-stage ignition	00.02.43	Armstrong's first step on moon	109.24
Second-stage shutdown	00.09.12	Aldrin's first step on moon	109.42
Third-stage ignition	00.09.15	End of moonwalk	111.40
Earth orbit insertion	00.11.50	Lunar liftoff	124.22
Start translunar injection burn	02.44.15	Docking in lunar orbit	128.04
End translunar injection burn	02.50.13	Transearth injection	135.25
		Return phase	
Lunar environment phase		Service Module jettisoned	194.49
Lunar orbit insertion	75.50.00	Re-entry into earth's atmosphere	195.03
Lunar orbit circularization	80.05.00	Splashdown	195.18

*Time from launch, 00.00.00 (hours. minutes. seconds); corresponds to 9:32 a.m. EDT, July, 1969.

temperatures around 5,000 degrees. In the crew compartment, however, it was only 80 degrees.

Like a man-made meteor, *Columbia* flew almost 1,800 miles after re-entry, arcing over Australia and the Coral Sea toward its touchdown point near Johnston Island in the mid-Pacific. At 180,000 feet altitude, the lifting action of the conical base forced the Command Module upward, back toward space. Armstrong permitted it to climb briefly, then he spoiled the lift by rolling the module, and a new descent began. Firing almost continuously to maintain stability and control the degree of lift, the thrusters kept *Columbia* on course toward the target.

At 24,000 feet, by which time air resistance had slowed the spacecraft to about 325 miles per hour, the parachute landing system went into action. A device capable of sensing altitude by measuring barometric pressure triggered the sequence. First, a portion of the outer spacecraft wall at the tip of the cone was jettisoned, exposing the parachute storage well. A pair of small chutes called *drogues*—meaning "anchors"—popped out to stabilize the Command Module and to reduce descent speed further, to about 125 miles per hour.

At about 10,000 feet, the three enormous main parachutes were deployed; the third represented an extra margin of safety because two of them could have lowered *Columbia*. Its descent speed down to about 20 miles per hour, *Columbia* splashed in the Pacific at 195 hours 18 minutes Ground Elapsed Time.

At the very end of a near-perfect voyage came one minor mishap: parachute drag flipped the Command Module over so that it was nose-down in the water. It posed no problem, only a brief period of discomfort; Collins activated a trio of flotation bags stowed in the nose, and their inflation righted the spacecraft in 5 minutes. An hour after splashdown, the astronauts were hoisted aboard a helicopter and delivered to the recovery ship USS *Hornet*.

In the brief span of 8 days, the magnificent men of Apollo 11 had flown more than half a million miles, entered the gravitational field of another celestial body, and walked upon its alien, forbidding surface. They had opened a door to the mysteries of the universe. They had provided inspiration for man's inevitable exploration of other planets. And they had demonstrated that anything man can imagine he can accomplish. Apollo 11 was, indeed, "one giant leap for mankind."

CONVERSION TABLES

NAUTICAL MILES TO STATUTE MILES

NAUTICAL MILES	STATUTE MILES
1	1.1508
2	2.3016
3	3.4524
4	4.6032
5	5.7540
6	6.9048
7	8.0556
8	9.2064
9	10.3572
10	11.5080
20	23.0160
30	34.5240
40	46.0320
50	57.5400
60	69.0480
70	80.5560
80	92.0640
90	103.5720
100	115.0800
200	230.1600
300	345.2400
400	460.3200
500	575.4000
600	690.4800
700	805.5600
800	920.6400
900	1,035.7200
1,000	1,150.8000
2,000	2,301.6000
3,000	3,452.4000
4,000	4,603.2000
5,000	5,754.0000
6,000	6,904.8000
7,000	8,055.6000
8,000	9,206.4000
9,000	10,357.2000
10,000	11,508.0000
20,000	23,016.0000
30,000	34,524.0000
40,000	46,032.0000
50,000	57,540.0000
60,000	69,048.0000
70,000	80,556.0000
80,000	92,064.0000
90,000	103,572.0000
100,000	115,080.0000
200,000	230,160.0000
300,000	345,240.0000
400,000	460,320.0000
500,000	575,400.0000
600,000	690,480.0000
700,000	805,560.0000
800,000	920,640.0000
900,000	1,035,720.0000
1,000,000	1,150,800.0000

FEET PER SEC. TO MILES PER HOUR

FEET PER SECOND	MILES PER HOUR
1	.6818
2	1.3636
3	2.0454
4	2.7272
5	3.4090
6	4.0908
7	4.7726
8	5.4544
9	6.1362
10	6.8180
15	10.2270
20	13.6360
25	17.0450
30	20.4540
35	23.8630
40	27.2720
45	30.6810
50	34.0900
55	37.4990
60	40.8480
65	44.3170
70	47.7260
75	51.1350
80	54.5440
85	57.9530
90	61.3620
95	64.7710
100	68.1800
125	85.2250
150	102.2700
175	119.3150
200	136.3600
300	204.5400
400	272.7200
500	340.9000
1,000	681.8000
2,000	1,363.6000
3,000	2,045.4000
4,000	2,727.2000
5,000	3,409.0000
10,000	6,818.0000
15,000	10,227.0000
20,000	13,636.0000
25,000	17,045.0000
30,000	20,454.0000
35,000	23,863.0000
40,000	27,272.0000
45,000	30,681.0000
50,000	34,090.0000

NOTE: intermediate figures in both tables can be found by addition

Apollo Glossary

Ablative material, special heat-dissipating material on the surface of a spacecraft that can be vaporized or melted during re-entry.

Abort, the cutting short of an aerospace mission before it has accomplished its objective.

Acceleration, the rate at which velocity increases.

Accelerometer, an instrument that senses acceleration forces along all three axes and converts them into electrical signals for controlling, measuring, indicating, or recording purposes.

Acquisition, the process of locating an orbiting space vehicle to begin tracking or gathering telemetry data.

Actuator, a device that transforms an electrical signal into a mechanical motion using hydraulic or pneumatic power.

Aerozine, a liquid fuel composed of 50% monomethylhydrazine and 50% unsymmetrical dimethylhydrazine.

Aft, toward the rear; in the Command Module, toward the blunt bottom.

AOS, acquisition of signal (e.g., when the Apollo spacecraft comes from behind the moon).

Apogee, that point in an orbit at which a satellite is farthest from earth.

Apolune, that point in a lunar orbit at which a spacecraft is farthest from the moon.

Attitude, the position of a vehicle as determined by the inclination of its axes to some frame of reference; for Apollo, an inertial, space-fixed reference is used.

Axis (plural, **axes**), any of three straight lines about which a spacecraft rotates; one of a set of reference lines for a coordinate system.

Azimuth, an arc of the horizon measured between a fixed point (usually true north) and the vertical circle through the center of an object.

Backup, an item or system available as replacement for one that fails; a backup crew is trained to replace the prime crew for an Apollo mission in the event of illness.

Boilerplate, a full-sized replica that has all of the mechanical characteristics of the true craft but none of the functional features.

Bulkhead, a dome-shaped part which encloses the end of a propellant tank.

Burnout, the point when combustion ceases in a rocket engine.

Burn time, the length of the thrusting period when engines are firing.

Canard, a short, stubby, wing-like part attached to a spacecraft to provide better stability in air.

Capcom, Capsule Communicator; the official at Mission Control Center (usually an astronaut) who communicates directly with the spacecraft crew.

Centrifugal force, a force which is directed away from the center of rotation; balances gravity in keeping a spacecraft in orbit.

Checkout, a sequence of operational and measurement tests to determine the condition and status of a system.

Cluster, two or more engines bound together to function as one propulsive unit.

CM, Command Module.

Configuration, shape; the figure or pattern formed by relative position of various items (e.g., the transposition maneuver puts the modules in lunar configuration).

Console, a grouping of controls, indicators, and similar electrial or mechanical equipment.

Control system, a system that serves to maintain attitude stability during forward flight and to correct deflections.

Cryogenic, supercold; refers to fuels or oxidizers that are liquid only at very low temperatures.

CSM, Command and Service Modules, when combined as a unit.

Delta V, velocity change.

Drogue, the hollow part of a connector into which another part, the probe, fits. (In the landing system, "drogue" refers to the small "anchor" parachutes which deploy to stabilize and slow the craft before the main chutes are released.)

DSKY, Display and keyboard (referred to by astronauts as "disky."

ECS, Environmental control system.

Escape velocity, the speed a body must attain in order to overcome a gravitational field; at the earth's surface, 36,700 feet per second.

EVA, extravehicular activity.

Explosive bolts, bolts surrounded by an explosive charge which can be activated by an electrical impulse, such as used to separate two rocket stages.

Extravehicular, occurring or located outside the vehicle.

Fairing, a piece, part, or structure having a smooth, streamlined outline, used to smooth a junction.

Footprint, the total area of possible landing points of a spacecraft.

Forward, toward the front; in the Command Module, toward the apex of the cone.

Free-return trajectory, a return to earth without power; would be used in the event of a failure of the service propulsion system.

G force, that force exerted upon an object by gravity or by reaction to acceleration or deceleration: one G is the measure of the gravitational pull required to move a body at the rate of about 32.16 feet per second.

G & N, guidance and navigation system.

Gimbal, a mechanical frame containing two mutually perpendicular intersecting axes of rotation, on which an engine or thruster can change thrust direction.

Gravitation, that force of attraction that exists between all particles of matter everywhere in the universe.

Gravity, that force which tends to pull bodies toward the center of mass, giving the bodies weight.

Ground Elapsed Time, time from the beginning of a mission.

Guidance system, a system which measures and evaluates flight information, correlates this with target data, converts the result into the conditions necessary to achieve the desired flight path, and communicates this data as commands to the flight control system.

Helium, the gas used in spacecraft and launch vehicle to pressurize propellant tanks and lines.

Honeycomb sandwich, construction in which the space between upper and lower surfaces is occupied by a strengthening material of a structure resembling a honeycomb.

Hypergolic, igniting spontaneously upon contact of fuel and oxidizer, thus eliminating the need for an ignition system.

IU, Instrument Unit.

Launch window, the period during which launch must occur if the vehicle is to accomplish its mission; the period's limits are established by such things as earth and moon position, launch vehicle capabilities, sunlight conditions, and recovery considerations.

LES, launch escape system.

Lifting body, a wingless body which achieves stability and lift from its shape alone.

LM, Lunar Module.

LOI, lunar orbit insertion.

LOS, loss of signal (e.g., when the Apollo spacecraft goes behind the moon).

Mare, a large, relatively flat area on the moon (Latin for "sea").

Mass, a measure of the quantity of matter in a body, usually in reference to a standard, such as earth's mass.

Max Q, maximum dynamic pressure; the point during launch when the vehicle is subjected to its severest aerodynamic strain.

Micrometeoroid, a solid particle of matter traveling in space at considerable speed and measuring less than 1/250th of an inch in diameter.

MSFN, Manned Space Flight Network.

n.mi., nautical mile, about 1.15 statute miles (see Table on page 152).

Nominal, occurring just as planned.

Orbit, a spacecraft's path around earth or other body, beginning and ending at a fixed point in space and covering 360 degrees of travel; the point on earth above which an orbit begins is not the same as where it ends because the earth also is revolving.

Orbital velocity, the velocity necessary to maintain an orbit against the pull of gravity.

Oxidizer, in a rocket propellant, a substance such as liquid oxygen or nitrogen tetroxide that yields oxygen for burning the fuel.

Parking orbit, orbit around the earth or moon in which a spacecraft can wait for the proper moment for translunar or transearth injection.

Payload, the item or items (e.g., a space-craft) lifted into space by the launch vehicle.

Perigee, that point in an orbit at which a satellite is nearest earth.

Perilune, that point in a lunar orbit at which a spacecraft is nearest the moon.

Pitch, the movement of a space vehicle about an axis (usually labeled "Y") that is perpendicular to its longitudinal axis.

Pitchover, the maneuver in which the launch vehicle turns from vertical flight to a more horizontal direction.

Pressure vessel, the capsule, a pressurized cabin which has an atmosphere tolerable to man or other living things.

RCS, reaction control system, the system of small thrusters which fire to control the attitude of a spacecraft.

Real time, as it happens, used in connection with data collection to distinguish it from stored data.

Re-entry corridor, the region through which a spacecraft must pass for successful re-entry, limited by altitude and velocity.

Reference trajectory, the planned flight path, to which a flight control computer compares actual flight movements.

Retrorocket, a rocket that gives thrust in a direction opposite to the direction of the object's motion.

Revolution, circuit of the earth or moon beginning and ending at a fixed point on earth; because earth is also revolving, it is more than 360 degrees.

Rill, a long, narrow trench on the moon's surface.

Roll, a movement of a space vehicle about its longitudinal axis.

S-band, a radio-frequency band of 1550 to 5200 megacycles per second.

Sensor, a sensing element, such as that portion of a navigational system which perceives deviations from a reference and converts them into signals.

SLA, Spacecraft-Lunar Module Adapter.

SM, Service Module.

Solar flare, violent, sudden disturbance of the sun's surface, resulting in a sharp increase in high-energy radiation, or ionized particles, called the *solar wind.*

Solid rocket, a rocket using a propellant containing fuel and oxidizer combined into a solid plastic-like cake.

Specific impulse, a means of determining rocket performance; it is equivalent to the effective exhaust velocity divided by gravity and is expressed in pounds thrust per pounds fuel per second.

Staging, the separation of one stage from another.

Station-keeping, remaining in a precise orbit with a constant velocity; may be in relation to another spacecraft.

TEI, transearth injection.

Telemetering, a system for taking measurements within a space vehicle in flight and transmitting them by radio to a ground station.

Terminator, the line separating the sunlit and dark portions of the earth or moon.

Thrust, the force developed by a rocket engine, measured by multiplying the propellant mass flow rate by the exhaust velocity relative to the vehicle, expressed in pounds.

Thruster, a small engine in the reaction control system used for attitude control.

TLI, translunar injection.

Trajectory, the flight path traced by a vehicle under power or as a result of power.

Translunar, the phase of flight between the earth and moon.

Transposition, the rearrangement in space of the three Apollo modules once the need for aerodynamic considerations is past.

UDMH, unsymmetrical dimethylhydrazine.

UHF, ultra-high frequency.

Ullage, the volume in a closed tank or container above the surface of a stored liquid.

VAB, Vertical Assembly Building.

VHF, very-high frequency.

Yaw, movement of a space vehicle from its vertical axis.

Index

Ablation, *illus.*, 42
Ablation effects, *illus.*, 41
Ablative material, 42, 73; *illus.*, 41
Abort flights, 99, 106
Abort modes, *illus.*, 100
Adapter, *see* Lunar Module adapter
Aerodynamic lift, *illus.*, 39
Aerojet-General Corporation, 49
Aero Spacelines, 67
Aerozine-50, 49
Air, 36
Air Force search/rescue airplanes, 83
Airframe (Saturn V), 19
Airless flight, 36
Airplane, comparison with Apollo, 36
Air resistance, 39
Aldrin, Edwin E. "Buzz", 120-151; *illus.*, 85, 121, 125, 140, 141, 150
Alphonsus Crater, 93
Analysis of rock samples, 87-89
Anders, William A., 110; *illus.*, 111
Anechoic chamber, *illus.*, 102
Antennas, 30-foot, 77
85-foot deep-space, 80; *illus.*, 78
Anti-contamination, 84-86
Antigua tracking station, 80
Apollo 1, 103, 104
Apollo 2, 103
Apollo 3, 103
Apollo 4, 105-108, 109, 113, 118; *illus.*, 108
Apollo 5, 105, 108, 118
Apollo 6, 109, 113, 118
Apollo 7, 110, 118; *illus.*, 32
Apollo 8, 90, 96, 110-113, 118; *illus.*, 75, 111, 112
Apollo 9, 114, 118; *illus.*, 115, 116
Apollo 10, 96, 117-119; *illus.*, 13, 37, 62, 81, 97, 117, 118

Apollo 11, 85, 118, 119, 120-151; *illus.*, 120-151; *table*, 150
Apollo fire, 106; *illus.*, 104
Apollo program,
cost, 10
impact, 14
origins, 8
Apollo/Range Instrumented Aircraft, 80; *illus.*, 76
Apollo spacecraft, 31, 36-51; *illus.*, 29, 68
comparison with Mercury and Gemini, 11
see Command Module, Lunar Module, Service Module
Apollo spacecraft engine, *see* Service Propulsion System
Armstrong, Neil, 120-151; *illus.*, 85, 125, 137, 141, 143, 150
Ascension Island tracking station, 80
Ascent engine, 58, 113, 119, 146
Ascent stage, 54, 57-63, 109, 115, 136; *table*, 56; *illus.*, 59, 62, 145
Atlas-Agena, 92
Atlas ballistic missile, 22
Atlas-Centaur, 92
Atlas launch vehicle, 11
Atmosphere, 18, 36, 148
Attenuation structure, 43
Automated test equipment, 96
Automatic checkout system, 74
Auxiliary propulsion modules (S-IVB), 32-33

Backup systems, 62
Bacterial contamination, 84
"Barbeque mode," 113
Barge, *illus.*, 68
Barge terminal, Kennedy Space Center, 67
Bell Aerosystems Company, 58

Bennington, USS, 107
Bermuda tracking station, 80
"Big Shot" (Apollo 4), 105
Biological isolation garments, *illus.*, 150
Biological laboratory, 87
Biological tests of lunar samples, *illus.*, 88
Boeing Company, The, 27
Boeing Stratocruiser, 67
Boilerplates, 99, 100, 106
Borman, Frank, 110
Braking phase, of descent, 134
Bulk sample, 139

Canary Island tracking station, 80
Canberra tracking station, 80
Cape Kennedy, 64, 120, 149; *illus.*, 65
Carnarvon tracking station, 80
Centrifugal force, 19
Cernan, Eugene A., 117, 119; *illus.*, 81
Chaffee, Roger B., 104, 105, 144
Checkout, 67
Chronology of Apollo, *tables*, 106, 118
Clustering of engines, 23
Cold soak, 107, 109, 113
Collins, Michael, 120-151; *illus.*, 125, 150
Columbia, 126, 127, 130, 131-151
Command and Service Modules, *illus. & tables*, 44-45
Command Module, 36-49, 50, 51, 54, 58, 61, 69, 70, 83, 99, 100, 103, 104, 106, 107, 109, 110, 114, 115, 118, 119, 131, 147, 149; *illus.*, 37, 41, 47; *table*, 44
control and display panel, *illus.*, 47

docking assembly, *illus.,* 43

fire, 105; *illus.,* 104

re-entry, *illus.,* 39

wall construction, *illus.,* 42

Communications, 58, 61, 64, 75, 77-83

Communications on moon, *illus.,* 82

Communications satellites, 80

Communications test, *illus.,* 102

Computer complex, Manned Spacecraft Center, 74

Computers, 49, 64, 69, 128, 130

Consoles, 74, 75

Contingency samples, 137

Control and display panel, Command Module, *illus.,* 47, 48

Lunar Module, *illus.,* 59

Core samples, 144

Corpus Christi tracking station, 80

Couches, 46; *illus.,* 48

Countdown, 74

Crawler, *illus.,* 72

Crawlerway, 70, 72

Crew compartment, 46, 58, 132

Cunningham, Walter, 110

Deceleration, 39, 149

Deep-space navigation, 113

Department of Defense, 83

Descent engine, 55, 108, 109, 115, 119, 132, 135

Descent phase, 132; *illus.,* 55, 133

Descent stage, 54-58, 63, 146; *table,* 56

Diamondback Rill, *illus.,* 131

Director of flight operations, 76

Display consoles, 46, 61; *illus.,* 47

Docking, 43, 61, 126, 147; *illus.,* 32, 43, 115

Documented samples, 144

Drag, 18

Drogue (docking), 61, 114; *illus.,* 43

Drogue parachute, 151

Eagle, 126, 131-151; *illus.,* 145

Early Apollo Scientific Experiments Payload, 88

Earth, 127, 129; *illus.,* 9, 111, 128

Earth-based complex, 64-83

Earth orbit, 77

Eisele, Donn F., 110

Environmental control system, 48, 58, 66, 107, 113

Essex, USS, 110

Experiments, 58, 88; *illus.,* 89, 142

Experiments officer, 76

Extravehicular activity, 114

Extravehicular visor, 136; *illus.,* 141

F-1 engine, 22-24, 105; *illus.,* 22, 23, 25; *table,* 32

Firing rooms, 66, 69

First stage, *see* S-IC first stage

Flag, American, 139; *illus.,* 149

Flame trench, 72

Flight control computer, 34

Flight-rated spacecraft, 106

Flight suit, 46

Flight tests, 98-119

Flotation bags, 151

Footprints, *illus.,* 138

Free-return trajectory, 124

Fuel, energy value, 24

Fuel cell, 50

Fueling, 74

Fuel tank (S-IC), 27

Gagarin, Yuri, 144

Garrett Corporation, AiResearch Manufacturing Division, 46

Gemini program, 10, 11, 42, 46, 48, 107

G forces, 39

Goddard Space Flight Center, 78, 80

Goldstone tracking station, 78, 80; *illus.,* 78

Grand Bahama Island tracking station, 80

Gravity, 18, 19, 39, 112, 116

Grissom, Virgil I., 104, 105, 144

Ground Elapsed Time, 123

Ground support, 64-83

Ground tests, 98

Grumman Aircraft Engineering Corp., 38

Guam tracking station, 80

Guaymas tracking station, 80

Guidance and navigation controls, 48, 58; *illus.,* 47

Guidance computer, 34, 127, 129, 147

Gumdrop (Apollo 9), 116

H-1 engines, 101

Hamilton Standard Division, United Aircraft Corporation, 61

Hatch, 61

Hawaii tracking station, 80

Heat of re-entry, *see* Re-entry heating

Heat shield, 42, 149; *illus.,* 41, 42

Heat shield tests, 103, 104, 107

High bay (VAB), 66

High-gain antenna, 113

Hold-down arms, 69, 74

Honeycomb construction, 30, 40, 42, 49

Hornet, USS, 151

Huntsville, USNS, 78

Hypergolic propellants, 49

IBM Federal Systems Division, 34

Inertial guidance unit, 49

Inertial platform, 34

Insertion, 50, 113

Instrument Unit, 34, 48, 51, 69, 105, 107, 123, 124, 126, 127; *illus.,* 28, 33

Insulation, 31, 40; *illus.,* 42

Interstage, 30

J-2 engines, 24-27, 30, 31, 33, 105, 107, 109, 123, 124; *illus.,* 25, 26

Kennedy, John F., 8, 106

Kennedy Space Center, 31, 64-74

Kerosene, 24

Komarov, Vladimir, 144

Landing legs, 58

Landing phase, of descent, 134-135; *illus.,* 133

Landing radar, 58, 119, 132

Landing site, 90-95; *illus.*, 95, 118
Landing Site Number Two, 119, 132; *illus.*, 131, 135
Land stations, 77
Laser ranging retro-reflector, 144; *illus.*, 89
Launch, 51; *illus.*, 17
Launch azimuth, 80
Launch Complex 39, 64-74; *illus.*, 65, 66
Launch Control Center, 66, 120; *illus.*, 66, 73
Launch cost, 98
Launch escape system, 51, 98, 106, 123; *illus.*, 44-45, 100
Launch pad, 70, 72; *illus.*, 65
Launch vehicle, 16
Life-support backpack, 144
Lift, 38, 151
Lifting body, 38
Line of sight, 77
Liquid hydrogen, 24, 30, 103
Liquid oxygen, 19, 30
Little Joe II, 99, 106; *illus.*, 99
Lovell, James I., 9, 110
Low bay (VAB), 66
Lunar activity, 86
Lunar configuration, 114
Lunar landing mission, 120-151
Lunar Module, 38, 43, 52-63, 69, 94, 105, 106, 108, 109, 113, 114, 115, 117, 118, 131, 132, 144; *illus.*, 52, 56-57, 59
Lunar Module adapter, 61, 114, 126; *illus.*, 32
Lunar Module docking assembly, *illus.*, 43
Lunar orbit, 110, 117
Lunar Orbiter spacecraft, 90-95, 130; *illus.*, 92
Lunar orbit insertion, 129
Lunar Receiving Laboratory, 84-89; *illus.*, 88
Lunar surface, 93; *illus.*, 112, 117, 118
Lunar weight, 138

Madrid tracking station, 80
Manned Spacecraft Center, 74-76
Manned Space Flight Network, 77, 81, 82; *illus.*, 76
Mapping the moon, 90-95
Mare, 93
Marshall Space Flight Center, 106
Mass concentrations, 112
McDivitt, James A., 114, 115
McDonnell Douglas Corporation, 32
Medical officer, 76
Mercury program, 10, 11, 38, 42, 48, 107
Mercury-Redstone, 62
Mercury, USNS, 78
Merritt Island, 66
Merritt Island station, 80
Messages from earth's leaders, *illus.*, 142
Meteorite, 48
Michoud Assembly Facility, 67
Mid-course corrections, 128-129, 148
Mission control, 75, 128, 136, 144
Mission Control Center, 74, 75
Mission Operations Control Room, 75; *illus.*, 75
Mississippi Test Facility, 67
Mobile launch, 70
Mobile launcher, 69; *illus.*, 71
Mobile Quarantine Facility, 87; *illus.*, 86
Mobile service structure, 73, 74
Modules, 38
Moltke (crater), *illus.*, 131
Moon mapping, 90-95
Moon, scientific investigation, 14
Moon, statistics, *table*, 122
Moon, through telescope, *illus.*, 12

NASA Communications Network, *illus.*, 79
National Aeronautics and Space Administration, 10, 64
Navigation, 128
Navy, U.S., 83
Network controller, 76
Nitrogen tetroxide, 49
Nixon, Richard M., President, 139
North American Rockwell Corporation, Rocketdyne Div., 20
Space Division, 30, 38

Ocean of Storms, *illus.*, 94
Optical star-sighting system, 113
Optical unit, 49
Ordnance, 73
Oxidizer, 19
Oxidizer tank (S-IC), 28

Parachute, 46, 100, 151
Pegasus meteoroid detection satellite, 106
Phenolic epoxy, 42
Photographing moon, 90-95
Physical/chemical laboratory, 87
Pioneer spacecraft, 83
Plaque, commemorative, 138-139
Portable life support system, 61; *illus.*, 60
Pratt & Whitney Aircraft Co., 50
Prelaunch operations, 70
Preliminary Examination Team, 88
Pressure vessel, 40, 46, 54
Prime recovery ship, 83
Princeton, USS, 119; *illus.*, 81
Principal Investigators, 88
Probe (docking), 61, 114; *illus.*, 43
Propellants, 20, 27, 30
Proving flights, 96

Quarantine, 86

Radar, 77
Radioactivity, 87
Radio waves, 77
Ranger spacecraft, 90-93, 130; *illus.*, 92
Reaction control engines, 43, 49
Reaction engine, 19
Recovery, *illus.*, 81, 150
Recovery carrier, 87
Recovery forces, 83, 150
Redstone, USNS, 78, 80
Redundancy, 61-63
Re-entry, 38, 40, 113, 148; *illus.*, 39

Re-entry heating, 42, 51, 148; *illus.*, 41, 42
Re-entry velocity, 42, 109, 117
Reference trajectory, 34
Reliability, 48, 61-63, 116
Rendezvous and docking, 115, 119, 146
Rendezvous radar, 58, 115, 119, 146
Rescue, 146
Restart in space (S-IVB), 32
Retrorockets, 30
Rocket engine, *illus.*, 18
Rock samples, 84-89, 147; *illus.*, 143

S-IC first stage, 27-30, 67, 69, 105, 123; *illus.*, 22, 28-29
S-II second stage, 30-31, 67, 69, 105, 123; *illus.*, 25, 28-29, 68
S-IVB third stage, 31-34, 67, 69, 103, 105, 107, 108, 114, 118, 123, 124, 126, 127; *illus.*, 28-29, 32
Saturn I, 100, 105, 106
Saturn IB, 103, 104, 105, 106, 108, 110, 118; *illus.*, 101
Saturn V launch vehicle, 16-35, 40, 53, 105, 113, 118, 120; *illus.*, 17, 21, 28-29, 108
Saturn V/Apollo stack; *illus.*, 28-29, 71
Schirra, Walter M., Jr., 110
Schweickart, Russell, 114, 115, 116
Scott, David R., 114; *illus.*, 116
Sea of Clouds, 93
Sea of Tranquillity, 93, 95, 119, 132; *illus.*, 118, 131
Second stage, *see* S-II second stage
Seismometer, 144; *illus.*, 89
Service Module, 38, 49-51, 69, 70, 83, 99, 100, 103, 106, 107, 110, 114, 118, 126, 127, 131, 148; *illus.*, 44-45

Service Propulsion System, 49, 63, 103, 106, 118, 130; *illus.*, 50
Sleeping stations, 46
Solar flare, 83
Solar Particle Alert Network, 83
Solar radiation, 83
Solar wind equipment, 88, 139, 144
Soviet Union, 8
Soyuz 1, 144
Spacecraft, 16
Spacesuit, 60, 127; *illus.*, 60, 102
Space vehicle, 16
Space walk, 116
SPAN, 83
Spanish peninsula, 128
Spider (Apollo 9), 116
Splashdown, 39, 151; *illus.*, 97
Stack, 16, 98
Stafford, Thomas P. 117, 119
Stages, Saturn V, *illus.*, 21
Staging, 20, 24
Suits, thermal, 61
Supercritical maneuvers, 113, 119, 129, 132, 146, 148
Super Guppy, 67; *illus.*, 67
Surface bearing of moon, 93
Surveyor spacecraft, 90-95, 130; *illus.*, 92
Swing arms, 69
Systems engineers, 76

Technology, impact on, 14
Telecasts, 118; *illus.*, 111
Telemetry system, 75
Television camera, 139
Temperature, 40, 113
Test facilities, 96
Test program, 96-119
Thermal control, 127
Thermal garment, 61, 136; *illus.*, 60
Third stage, *see* S-IVB third stage
30-foot antenna, 80
Three-stage launch vehicle

liftoff thrust, *table*, 18
Thrust, 19
Thrusters, 38, 49, 58, 113
Thrust requirements, *table*, 18
Thrust structure, S-IC, 27
Time-dependent studies, 87
Titan II launch vehicle, 11
Tracking, 77-83
Tracking aircraft, 79-80
Tracking ships, 78
Tracking stations, 64, 75, 113, 128, 130; *illus.*, 76
Tranquillity Base, 135, 136, 139
Transearth injection, 147
Translunar injection, 124
Transporter, 70, 72; *illus.*, 71, 72
Transposition and docking, 114; *illus.*, 115
TRW Inc., 54
Turnaround maneuver, 114, 126; *illus.*, 32, 115
Two-stage launch vehicle liftoff thrust, *table*, 18
Tycho Crater, *illus.*, 91

Ullage motors, 31, 33, 123
United Kingdom, 128
Uprated Saturn, *see* Saturn IB
U.S. 1 (rill), *illus.*, 131

Van Allen radiation belts, 83
Vanguard, USNS, 78, 80
Vertical Assembly Building, 66, 68, 70; *illus.*, 66
Visibility phase, of descent, 134

Weight changes in staging, *table*, 21
Wet run, 74
White, Edward H., II, 104, 105, 144
White Sands Test Range, 99

Young, John W., 117, 119

Zero speed abort, 99

The Author

James J. Haggerty is one of the few writers who has been covering space research since before Sputnik I opened the Space Age. An ex-pilot living in Washington, D.C., he is the author of ten books and numerous encyclopedia articles on aviation and space and serves as Editor of *The Aerospace Year Book* for the Aerospace Industries Association. Mr. Haggerty has won a number of major writing awards and is a former president of the Aviation/Space Writers Association.

Typography for this book was done by American Graphics Corporation. The text is 10 point Melior.